GIS Guidebook:

Building Web Maps and Apps with ArcGIS Online

For Disaster Response and Other Critical Uses

By David W. Allen, GISP

GIS Guidebooks Press

Published by GIS Guidebooks Press

www.GISGuidebooks.com

Corsicana, TX

info@GISGuidebooks.com

ISBN-13: 978-0-578-70562-0

GIS Guidebook: Building Web Maps and Apps with ArcGIS Online
for Disaster Response and Other Critical Uses
Table of Contents

About the Author

David Allen has been working with GIS since 1983, developed the GIS system for the City of Euless and has worked there over 31 years, taught evening classes in the GIS program at Tarrant County College for over 19 years, and has published seven other bestselling books on GIS. He knows this stuff inside and out ... and he has a great knack at being able to explain complex topics in a simple way. He helped found the Texas Emergency GIS Response Team in 2006 and currently serves as it's State Director of Operations in addition to overseeing all the training programs. In this capacity he has responded to every major disaster in Texas either on-site or via remote mapping, handling the mapping chores for tornadoes, floods, hurricanes, and all types of disasters. The lessons learned about training and response are included in this text.

Chapter 11 – Putting It All Together

Author's Introduction

This book was originally developed as a training guide for the Texas Emergency GIS Response Team – a nonprofit group consisting of GIS professionals who handle disaster mapping in Texas. But after looking over the materials, I felt that this would be of benefit to anyone wanting to do disaster mapping. Plus the proceeds from the book will go into the coffers of Texas EGRT and help us fund new equipment and cover our costs during deployments.

But as I look over the Table of Contents, I think you will find that these lessons would be applicable for most any situation – not just disasters. Instead of doing a Quick Capture app for reporting damage you might make one for public infrastructure that might need repair (leaking fire hydrants or damaged street signs). Or use Survey 123 to collect specimen tree locations in the forest instead of cataloging tornado damage.

However you use these materials, I hope it will help with whatever project you have going.

The book is laid out in such a way as to step you through the process of making local data from your desktop into ArcGIS Online (AGOL) layers – then using those layers in maps, applications, dashboards, and who knows what else. The book includes hands-on exercises for you to complete as well as extensions to those exercises that you can complete on your own. All the exercises are totally fabricated to demonstrate certain techniques – so although they are based in reality the data itself is not relevant in any situation. I made it all up.

Throughout the book you will also see "Rafael's Question", which is a question students typically ask in the classroom except in this situation I have to both ask and answer them. You will also find "Rafael's Challenge" at the end of the book where you will take techniques you've learned and apply them to new projects with minimal instruction. Helpful tips are given that you can reference as you solve the dilemma.

Have fun learning this – and be ready for the next disaster.

The exercise data and materials for this book can be downloaded using the DropBox link found on this page:

http://GISGuidebooks.com/AGOL

I always say this at the end of the Texas EGRT training classes:

"It's OK to have fun playing and experimenting with these new tools. Get over the learning curve and get your mistakes out of the way. During a real deployment you need to act professionally and do your job quickly and efficiently. The EOC is a pressure cooker and its serious business. Some people have just had the worst day of their lives … some people have just had the last day of their lives. But when I'm in there working hard to make the situation better I'll be damn proud to have you next to me!" - DWA

Chapter 1 – Signing in to ArcGIS Online

The Basics of your Account

It all starts with signing in to your account. If you don't have an account, check with your system administrator, or if you are working through this on your own you could get a free trial account.

You can sign in at the URL **ArcGIS.com**

You may also have an organizational account and log in through their URL. For Texas EGRT the URL is

TexasEGRT.maps.arcgis.com .

Whichever you do, you will need a username and a password.

Your login will also have been assigned a User Type and a User Role. These can control what you are allowed to do with items in the organization.

The User Types are:

> Viewer – can see items but can create, edit, or share them.
>
> Editor – can see and edit items, but can't create new items or change the sharing permissions.
>
> Field Worker – mostly used for accounts that will be using field based apps, these users can see and edit items, but can't create new items or change the sharing permissions. They also have permissions to the Field Apps Bundle.
>
> Creator – can see, edit, create, and share items as well as some rights to administer the organization.
>
> GIS Professional – this user type can pretty much do anything, as well as access the organization's ArcGIS Pro licenses.

The hierarchy of users gives you control over what permissions members have. As an example, during a deployment you may have two GIS professionals that will be designing and created maps and apps in both AGOL and ArcGIS Pro; two creators that will be working within AGOL to manage the feature layers maps, and apps; and 25 field workers who will be using a Survey 123 damage assessment app in the field. As things heat up, you may need to add some viewer accounts so that certain people can see the online maps without having the power to edit them.

Each user also has a role in the organization which can also be used to set permissions. These can be one of the default roles like Administrator or Creator, or can be a custom user role. The custom roles allow the administrator to build permissions from an ala-carte' menu for things like allowing a user to create or join a group on their own to having administrator privileges to assign access to licenses. As an example, the Texas EGRT organizational structure has a special role called EGRT Power User that allows members with this role to do almost anything except manage other user accounts. There will be one of these at every disaster – everyone else will have a lesser role depending on their needs.

You may also be allowed to log in under multiple user names either within your organization, or even outside organizations. To do this, click the user name in the upper right of the display and select Switch Accounts.

If you have logged in using other credentials in the past, they will be shown here. You can select any of these and login to link the account – or select the option at the bottom to link in a new account.

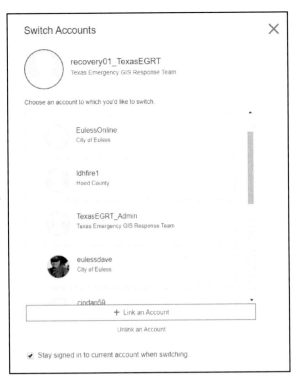

Note the selection at the bottom to stay logged in to the current account when switching.

If you are working between two agencies, it's best to leave this checked.

But if you are working within an agency and are stepping up to assume a role with higher privileges and don't intent to switch back, you should log out the existing account. It's also good form to log out of accounts from other agencies when your collaboration with them has ended.

This next section will examine the multiple tabs in AGOL, and they will be shown in more detail later.

The ArcGIS Online Menus

Once you log in, you will see your front page, or Home tab. These are customizable and this is the one for TexasEGRT.

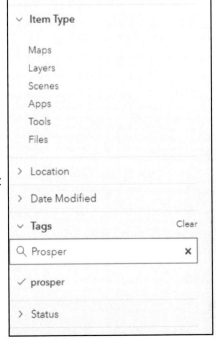

The Gallery tab is used to display and find all of the items you've made in your account. The gallery can be searched to find any specific item, but your best use of the Gallery is to set filters by Item Type or Tags.

Each item you create for a disaster deployment should have a tag for both the name of your agency and the disaster name. In this example, a filter under the Tags heading is set to find all items relating to PROSPER (a training exercise in the City of Prosper).

The results show all the items with the tag 'Prosper'. You can see where this can be helpful in finding just the items you are working for the current disaster.

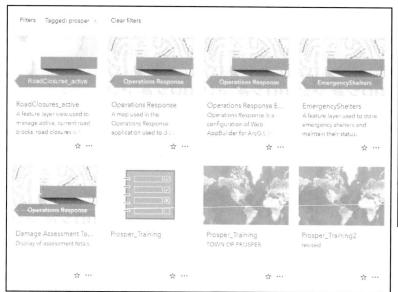

Rafael's Question – Can I use multiple filters?

Yes, you can stack filters of item type, location, data, and status. Just be careful because if you try to manage too many filters at a time you may find that nothing displays in your Gallery. Filtering by the tag for disaster name and the item type might be the best place to start – and if the list is still too long begin looking at adding other filters. And you can always search by the specific name of the item (if you know it).

The Map tab and the Scene tab are used to set up the view of your data – and those will be covered in much detail later in this book.

The Groups tab is used to set up operational groups of your organization's members. By adding members to groups you can control which items within the organization they will be able to see or edit. When you log in and select the Groups tab, you will see all the groups in which you are a member. In the image below you can see that the BOAT Team group and the SWRCC group can only be seen by members of the group. The Recovery Team group is viewable by the entire organization, although this will still require a login. And the Harvey group is public and can be seen by anyone even without a login. Note that the Group list can also be filtered to narrow down the groups shown.

There is a special type of group at the bottom. The TDEM EGRT Share Group is a group that was created in another ArcGIS Online organization but is being shared with the TexasEGRT organization.

Clicking on a group will display any content that has been created by any member of that group. This is a quick way to find data associated with your team or specific area of deployment. There are also tabs within the group summary that allow you to set the sharing and add (or remove) members.

Rafael's Question – can a member be in multiple groups, and how do I decide who goes into what group?

Yes members can be in several groups if the administrator allows it. For instance, the organization's administrator is probably in all the groups. Then the team lead on a disaster may be in the SWRCC group to manage the displays in the Regional Command Center, and also in the Recovery Team group to have access to the field collection data. In this example the BOAT Team group is set up for the Building Officials Association of Texas, so only members certified by their association can be members of their group.

Skipping ahead to the Organization tab, this tab allows the organization's administrators to monitor all the members, software, licenses, credits, and much more. These things won't be covered in this book but there is a lot of online help that can show what can be done here.

Finally is the Content tab. In this book, most of the work will be done on this and the Groups tab. Just like with the other tabs, you can set filters to limit the display of items. The other way to limit the display is to create a folder and view only items in a particular folder. For disaster work, it is advised that you make a new folder for the disaster, then create all the new data in that folder. If there is existing data that will be part of this disaster, you can either move it into the new folder or put a tag on it with the disaster name. Then you could view all of the items with the disaster's tag and see items across folders. There are many ways to organize your data within the Content tab, and these will be explored in the exercises.

Exercise 1a – Creating the Storage Framework

In this exercise you will create some items in AGOL that will become the storage areas for your work, and so that you can see what they look like. Make sure that you have a login to an AGOL account with a Creator level or higher. Although you won't need the materials for this exercise, now would be a good time to go ahead and download the materials for this book from http://GISGuidebooks.com/AGOL .

You can log in to your AGOL account either through *ArcGIS.com* or through your organization, which will have the address *ORGANIZATION_NAME.maps.arcgis.com*.

1 **Log in to your AGOL account using your credentials.**

If you are an administrator in the organization, you may be taken to the Organization tab automatically, or if not you may be presented with the Home tab.

First you will want to make a Group. Groups are used to organize your user accounts and control who has access to which datasets. For instance, you may have a group for your EOC response team members that gives them permissions to access and edit ANY of the data in the organization. Then you may want a group for members that will be doing field data collection that allows them to edit a dataset but not to create new ones or delete existing one. Remember that users can be members of multiple groups, so your field response team users might only be members of the Recovery Team group, but some of your EOC admin users can also be in the group.

And as you'll see later, data can be made available to multiple groups. This can get a little intricate in decide which to use, and more emphasis will be placed on this later.

2 **Click the Groups tab. In the left column click Create Group**

3 Name the group *YOUR_NAME's Disaster Exercises*. Provide a Summary stating that these files are for use with this book only, and add a tag called *GIS Guidebooks*.

Following the Tags you can see a list of questions that allow you to set certain parameters for the group. These concern who can view, join, or contribute content to the group as well as control what members can do within the group. For each question, the first choice is always the most restrictive with the last choice being the least restrictive. For disaster data, you want to balance out the privacy requirements of the data with the accessibility and use by team members. You will almost never make disaster data public because of the chances of mis-use or incorrect editing. Later you will see ways to make certain aspects of data viewable by the public when necessary.

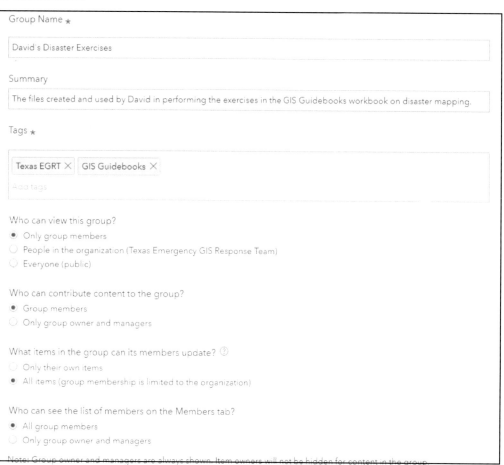

4 Under the question "Who can view this group?" change the response to *Only Group Members.* Then under the question "What items in the group can its members update?" change the response to *All items.*

With these setting, only members you specifically invite to the group can see the contents of the group, but any of those members can edit and contribute items to the group. In practice this is the best set-up for disaster data as long as you enforce group memberships.

5 If you like, you can drag and drop (or upload) a logo into the Thumbnail box to personalize your group.

6 Finally, click Create Group at the bottom.

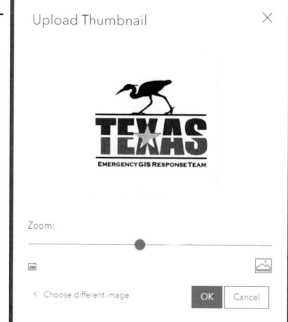

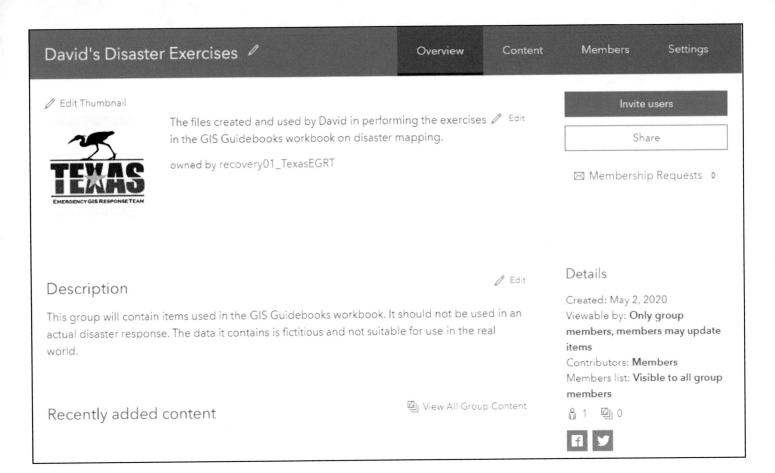

You can see information about the group as well as the tools invite other users to your group. The Share button will let you build a website that will display links to all the items you store in your group, with only group members able to access the web page using their own credentials. This is a good way to document the contents and provide users an easy way to find data.

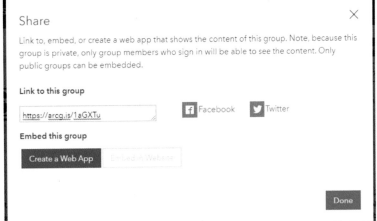

7 **Return to the Groups tab by clicking the Options button (three horizontal lines) and selecting Groups. If you want to try out the filters, try clicking Owner > Owned by Me or Date Created > Today.**

You can see how this might be useful if you have a lot of groups.

In the Texas EGRT environment, there is a group set up for Recovery Team (the EGRT members who will be working the disaster, BOAT Team (an affiliated group that does damage assessment), SWRCC (Southwest Regional Command Center), and TDEM EGRT SHARE GROUP (the group we use to share data with the State of Texas response agency).

Next you will want to make a folder. A folder is used to store information and datasets about a particular theme, and in our case a particular response. In practice it is a good idea to create a new folder for each disaster. This will help you filter the data to specific users when you have multiple disasters occurring simultaneously. As an example if you have a team responding to a flood event in Ellis County and a second team doing tornado damage assessments in Navarro County, you would want a folder for each event so that you can separate the data. The flood team doesn't need to see (or edit) the tornado damage layers that the other team is working with. And it would be a catastrophe if someone on the flood team deleted a layer from the tornado data because they didn't know what it was – and they weren't doing tornado damage assessments, so they didn't think it belonged with their data. You DO NOT want to be the one that has to go to the Incident Commander and tell them that the damage assessment teams have to go out again become someone accidently deleted the data.

8 Move to the Contents tab. On the left side of the screen is a column call Folders that is displaying all the existing folders (if any). Click the Create new Folder icon.

9 Name the folder *GIS Guidebooks - Disaster* and press OK.

All of the data you create for this book will go into this folder. You might even want to add a filter to the Folders list to display only this folder while you are working through this book.

There are no items in this folder … yet … but the next chapters will help you add new datasets.

10 If you are not continuing with the exercises, you can log out of your AGOL account.

Chapter 2 – Basic ArcGIS Online Components

Within AGOL there are three basic item types that you will deal with: Feature Layers, Web Maps, and Web mapping Applications. Dashboards and other types are discussed later.

Feature Layers

The Feature Layers are the actual datasets in your AGOL projects. These are the points, lines, and polygons that represent your real-world features. These can be created in AGOL from scratch, imported from ArcMap, served from ArcGIS Pro, brought in from a REST service, or imported from various other sources. As an example, you might have a file in a geodatabase that you are accessing in ArcMap or ArcGIS Pro that you want to use in AGOL. Or you may have been given a URL to a map service you're your own or another agency that you want to use. Or you may want to create a brand new feature layer using either your own schema or an existing Esri template. However you do it, the feature layer is the root of your item hierarchy. Everything else you create will work with a feature layer as its data source.

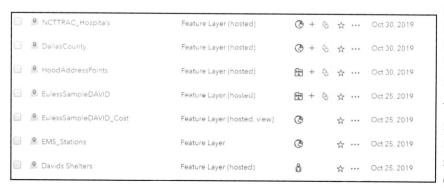

In this example below you can see several feature layers. The Content tab identifies the item type, but also shows more information about feature layers. A Hosted layer is one in which the data is stored in your AGOL account.

This might be data that you created, imported or served yourself. A layer not stamped as hosted means that the data is stored on someone else's server, such as data from the Esri Living Atlas or data that you brought in using a REST URL.

Those that also have the stamp View are a view-only copy of another feature layer. By creating a View of a feature layer, you can have one instance of the data that is protected and editable, and a "view" of the data that is not editable and therefore able to be shared publicly.

> **Rafael's Question – What about things like Excel spreadsheets and imagery?**
>
> Those things can be brought in to your AGOL account. The spreadsheets become Tables that can be managed much like the feature layers – you can add them to your apps and even edit them. Imagery can also be brought in and make an Imagery Layer. This is OK for a few images but for a large set of images covering an entire city, county, or larger area you might want to look at serving those through ArcGIS Enterprise or an existing online data source instead. Enterprise will allow for image caching, which will increase display performance, and AGOL will use a LOT of storage space (as well as storage credits). And although it won't be covered here, you can make any of these item types a Scene Layer, which is a 3D display layer.

Web Maps

Next up the chain of command is the Web Map. These are the map constructs that contain the visualizations of the feature layer data. When naming them, it is a good practice to include the word MAP at the end of the name. This will identify the item type even when you are in a display screen that doesn't identify it for you. It also avoids confusion with Web Map Applications.

A Web map can contain as many feature layers as you like, but you will see a practical limit on your maps when the refresh rate and map congestion become too much. As you add layers to a map, you can set the symbology, transparency, visibility range, and configure the pop-up window that displays when users click a features.

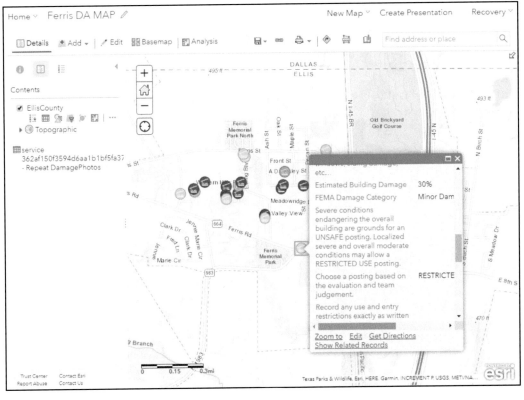

You will see that this is much like creating a Layout or Map in ArcMap or ArcGIS Pro. Many of the same techniques apply. This sample shows a Survey 123 layer in a Web map. Note that the symbology is set and an informational pop-up is configured.

Title								Modified	▼
☐ ▫ Damage Assessment Totals Dashboard	Dashboard		🔒	+	👥	☆	⋯	Dec 20, 2019	
☐ ▫ Operations Response EOC Application	Web Mapping Application		🔒	+	👥	☆	⋯	Dec 20, 2019	
☐ ▫ FerrisDASHBOARD	Dashboard		🌐			☆	⋯	Nov 22, 2019	
☐ ▫ Hood County Exercise App - Totals	Web Mapping Application		🔒	+	👥	☆	⋯	Nov 4, 2019	
☐ ▫ DallasTorndoMapDashBoard	Dashboard		🌐			☆	⋯	Oct 30, 2019	
☐ ▫ EulessDamageMAPDashboard	Dashboard		🔒			☆	⋯	Oct 25, 2019	
☐ ▫ EulessWebMAPBuildAPP	Web Mapping Application		🔒			☆	⋯	Oct 25, 2019	
☐ ▫ EulessDamageMAPApplication	Web Mapping Application		🔒			☆	⋯	Oct 25, 2019	
☐ ▫ DallasTorndoWebMapViewer	Web Mapping Application		🌐	+	👥	☆	⋯	Oct 21, 2019	

Web Applications

The Web Map certainly looks nice and care should be taken to make them attractive, but they don't have the functionality of a Web Map Application. Untrained users won't interact very well with a Web Map – they want a fancy application with better zoom tools, a simpler interface, and widgets to do things such as measure or search the attribute table. Web Map Applications are made from Web Maps in a variety of ways which might include using an existing template or employing the Web AppBuilder to create a custom app. Again, it is advisable to put the words WebApp or Web Map Application (or Dashboard in the case of Dashboards) to help distinguish these things in all situations.

Exercise 2a – Creating Items in a Content Folder

This exercise will step you through some quick creation steps to give you an idea of what the items will look like in your ArcGIS Online account.

1 If you have logged out of your AGOL account, log back in with the same credentials you used in Exercise 1.

2 Move to the Contents tab and select (or filter to) the GIS Guidebooks – Disaster folder.

Datasets can be added to your folder by either adding existing data from various sources or creating them from scratch. For this quick exercise you will create a Feature Layer and a Web map using simple templates.

3 Click Create button. Under the Create Features and More column select Feature layer.

Across the top of the display are the tabs From Template, From Existing Layer, and From URL. The important thing to remember here is that you are creating an EMPTY feature layer. If you choose any of the three tabs and select something the result will be an empty feature layer with the schema duplicated from the item you chose. EMPTY. If you want the data, you would have to use the Add Item selected at step 3!

For this exercise you will build a simple (empty) layer just to see the process. It won't be used for anything else.

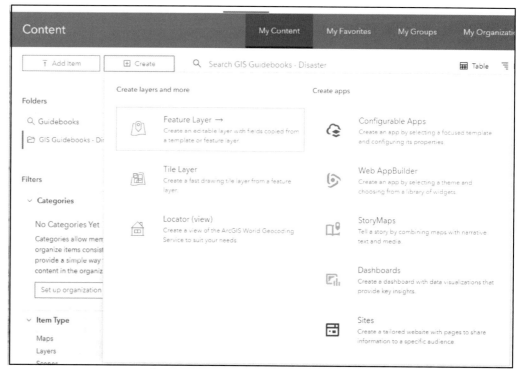

4 Under the From a Template tab, click Build A Layer. Select the Lines template and click Create.

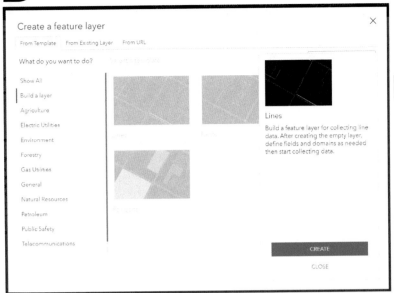

5 Click Next to begin adding the layer, zoom to a particular area of interest if you want and click Next.

6 Provide a title of *Sample Line Feature Layer*, then add tags and a summary. Make sure that it is being saved in the GIS Guidebooks – Disaster folder. Click Done.

When the feature layer is created you will be taken to that item's Details page. You will see dozens of buttons and settings (which will be covered later) but for now you will make a Web Map using this layer.

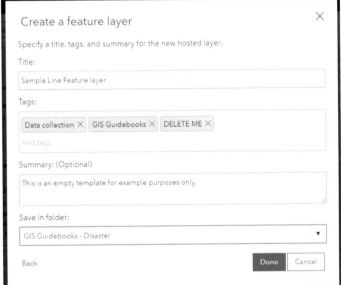

7 In the column on the right, click Open in Map Viewer.

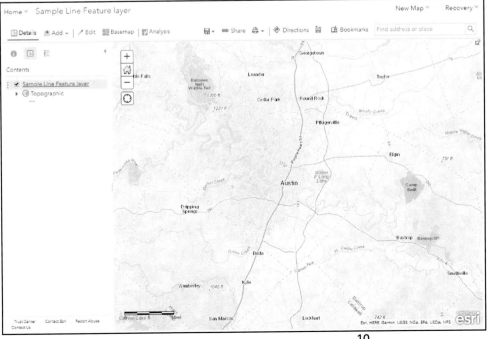

A new Web Map is created and zoomed to the extents of the feature layer you created. In the Contents column you will see the layer name and a default base map.

8 At the top of the map, click Save Map. Provide a map name using that name of the area you chose (ie. Austin Area Sample Map), tags, and a summary. Make sure it is saving in the correct folder. Note that you should include the word MAP in the title.

9 Return to the Content tab by clicking the drop-down area next to Home and selecting Content.

You will now see two items in your folder. The map can now be used to make a Web App.

10 Click the Options button (three dots) next to Austin Aera Sample MAP and select View Item Details.

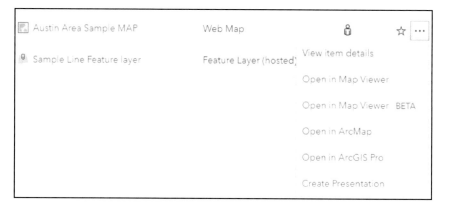

11 In the column on the right select Create Web App > Configurable Apps.

12 **From the list of templates select Basic Viewer, then click Create Web App.**

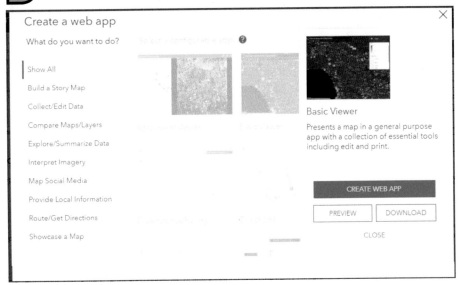

Note that the creation process will inherit the title, tags, and destination folder from the web map. It gives you the option of typing in a new summary, but if one isn't provided it will use the summary from the web map.

At this point it is recommended that the title be changed to include the words WEB APP to distinguish it in the contents list from the WEB MAP.

13 **In the title, change MAP to *WEB APP* and click Done.**

You will be taken to the web app configuration page where there are again dozens of settings (which will be covered later). For now you can try launching it if you want, or just close it to return to the Details page.

14 **Click the Close tab to return to the details page. Then click the Content tab.**

You can see that you now have three items in your folder. From here you can set all the parameters and sharing for the folders and manage all aspects of their use.

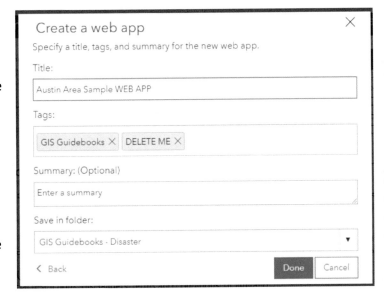

15 **Click the Gallery tab. In the left column click Tags and set a filter to GIS Guidebooks. All of your items will be displayed with a thumbnail, title, and summary.**

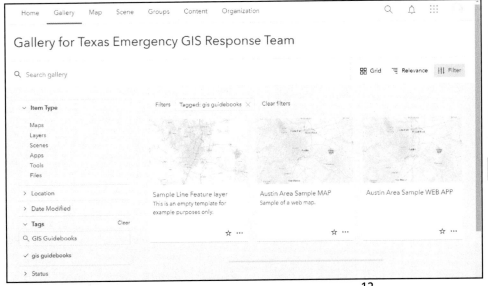

In this display you can see the value of adding MAP and WEB APP to the names of the items. If you had accepted the default title for the web app it would have been the same as the web map – but these are very different items!

16 **Click the WEB APP and try it out!**

This was a quick look into the overall structure of the types of features you can create – feature layer … web map … web map – and you should have a good idea of the hierarchy here. Later on you will make more robust examples of these items.

If you are not continuing, log out of your AGOL account.

Chapter 3 – Adding and Creating Data in ArcGIS Online

You've seen the basic framework of items in AGOL, but the items you created weren't configured and subsequently were of little use. In this chapter you will look at adding existing data into AGOL as well as creating new and meaningful feature layers from templates (or even from scratch).

The Living Atlas of the World

You will start by adding a layer from the Esri Living Atlas to your existing AGOL folder. The Living Atlas has a large array of datasets that are curated by Esri or by top data experts in their fields, and in fact you can contribute data to the Atlas and make it available to the world. The data is freely available as a web service, although you may find that some of the premium services will expend AGOL credits as you use them.

The Living Atlas can be found at https://livingatlas.arcgis.com/, and from there you can search the contents. There is a wide variety of data so you might start with a general term and narrow the search down as you see what data is available. For instance you may start with a search using the keyword "Airports", then look over the results to see which of the returned layers is closest to the data you require. Note that you will probably want Feature Layers or Tile Layers since you will be able to add these to your map. The other layers may be Web Maps or some other preconfigured display of the data, and you need to be able to add it to your own web map.

Still unsure of which layer to use? You can click on each layer and see the details of each data set. You might need to identify the geometry type (point, line or polygon), the fields the data contains, who maintains the data, when it was last updated, and much more.

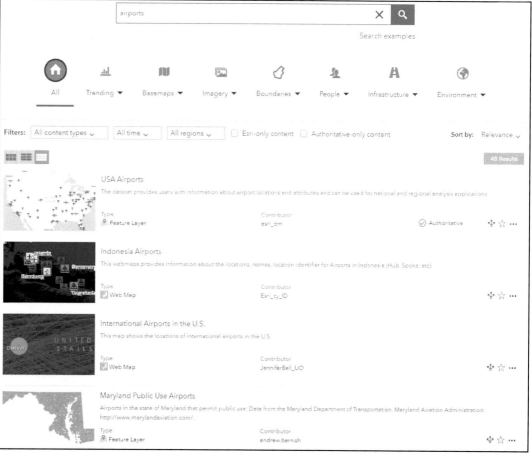

All of this, including a display of the live data, can be found on the details page. You can add the data to your own account using the provided URL in the layer details.

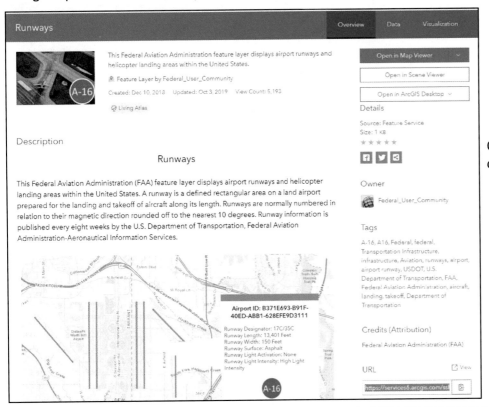

Once added to your account you can include it in web maps and apps.

Exercise 3a – Using Data from the Esri Living Atlas

In this scenario you would like to include a layer for Daytime Population. This can be very useful in disasters when the location is an urban business area (or even a college campus). The Census numbers show a population count for residents and doesn't account for workers who come into an area during the day then leave in the afternoon.

You will first need to see if there is such a dataset in the Living Atlas.

1 **Log in to your AGOL account and move to the Content tab. Set a filter or select the folder you created in the previous exercises.**

2 **Open a web browser and find the Esri Living Atlas website (either using the URL above or with a search). Enter the term _Population_ in the Atlas search tool.**

Three of the results look promising. One is titled 'USA 2016 Daytime Population'; one is titled 'Population Demographics in the United States', and its description mentions a date of 2018; and one is titled 'Population Change Due to Commuting'.

3 **Examine the details of the three search results above and decide which will be the best to use to show the daytime population of the disaster area.**

Rafael's analysis:

Population Change Due to Commuting – This layer only shows percent change and not total numbers. The disaster planning team will want hard counts to determine the magnitude of possible evacuation plans and shelter capacities. Plus this is a web map, not a web layer, so I can't add it to my own map.

Population Demographics in the United States – WOW – this dataset has so many interesting fields and breaks the data down into so many categories. It might be great for pre-disaster planning for older age groups or even to find concentrations of Millennials. I'll flag this one for future use but it doesn't have a field for daytime population counts so it won't help me here.

USA 2016 Daytime Population – it's not the most current data, BUT it does have specific counts for daytime and even breaks it down into daytime residents and daytime workers. It may be off by a few percentage points in the counts, but this is the layer to use.

This is a common result – there isn't the exact dataset you are looking for but you find something that is very usable. Remember, in a disaster ANY data is helpful if it can give relevant results. Now you will want to add this dataset to your AGOL folder.

4 **In the Living Atlas display, click the thumbnail for the USA 2016 Daytime Population layer. This will open the layer's detail display.**

5 **In the lower right area, look for the URL and click the Copy button.**

6 **Move to your AGOL Content display and select Add Item > From a URL.**

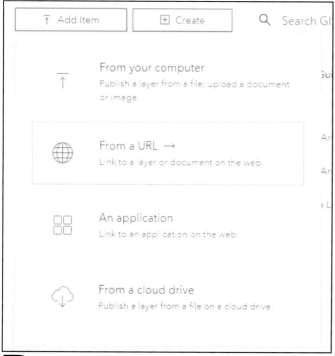

7 **Leave the Type selection as ArcGIS Server web service and paste the URL into the dialog. The Title will be set automatically. Set appropriate tags and click Add Item.**

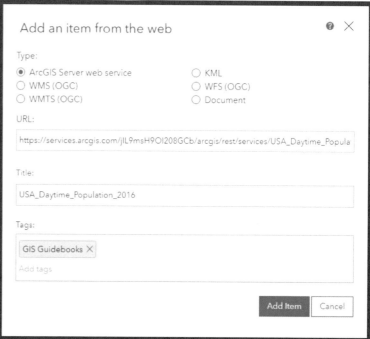

Once the item is added to your folder it will appear as a Feature Layer, just like the one you created earlier but with two major differences. Although this appears as one item in the Contents list and has the type Feature layer, you will see that it is not listed as 'Hosted'. This means that the data for this layer does not reside in your AGOL account but is hosted in another account.

15

The second major difference is that this single feature layer contains three datasets. If you look at the item's details you will see the three layers listed there; a States dataset, a Counties dataset, and a Tracts dataset. Note that these are all polygon layers. You will have access to all three of these layers, but it is your choice which ones to use in any web maps. You'll explore this data more later on.

8 Log out of your AGOL account and close the browser.

Rafael's Question: What happens if this data gets updated after I add it to my map?

That's the best part about using Living Atlas data. Remember that you aren't copying the data to your account, just serving up the data from someone else's account. And since the data is stored and curated by someone else, when they change it you will automatically see the changes in your maps and apps. One word of caution – check periodically for updates in case they archive this data as a snapshot in time and serve a new version of the data with a different name.

Sharing Data Through the Desktop Using ArcMap

Another way to get data into your ArcGIS Online account is through ArcMap. You can do this part of the exercise, but Rafael likes to use ArcGIS Pro for this (and you should make that transition, too). The steps include opening the data in ArcMap, then sharing as a web service. In this instance, a copy of the data is sent to your AGOL account AND STORED THERE! So any changes to the source data will not be reflected in the copy of the data you have made. Once you make your data into an AGOL feature layer, it is best if you switch all editing tasks to the AGOL version using an editing app instead of ArcMap. It is possible to serve updated data to AGOL and overwrite the copy you have made, but there are inherent dangers in doing this. First, any new data that you have entered through the AGOL editing tools or associated apps will be lost, and second, any changes that you may have made to the data structure (such as add or deleting fields) will corrupt any apps you have made using the data. So you really want to see this as a one-way street.

One other thing you'll note in using ArcMap is that all of the layers in the map document will be served up as a single feature layer with each ArcMap layer included as layers withing the feature layer. If you only want a single layer sent up as a feature layer, then it should be the only thing in the map document.

Exercise 3b – Creating a Feature Layer from ArcMap

For this exercise you will take one of the layers from an ArcMAP MXD file and make it into a feature layer. A copy of the data will then be hosted in the cloud.

If you have not already sone so, download the data used in this book using the DropBox link found on this page:

http://GISGuidebooks.com/AGOL

1 Open Exercise 3b.mxd from the supplied data.

In the file you will see several layers along with a base map. The red box graphic shows the area of the disaster, and for this you want the building footprints that fall within the red box. You will first create a temporary dataset of just the building footprints that you want, then make an MXD containing only that layer.

2 Select the building footprints that fall within the red box. Hint: use either the Select by Rectangle tool or the Select by Graphics tool.

Rafael's Question – Why are we splitting out a portion of the data? Can't we share it all to ArcGIS Online?

You absolutely could serve the entire county's dataset of building footprints. However, you would pay a cost in time trying to have your apps load this huge dataset, and you would pay the cost in dollars for storing that much data in the cloud. Anytime you can, you want to serve up only the data in the affected areas for a disaster.

3 Export the selected buildings into a layer called *Ft Worth Tornado Buildings* and store it in the Sample Disaster Data geodatabase that came with the book materials. When prompted, add the new layer to the map.

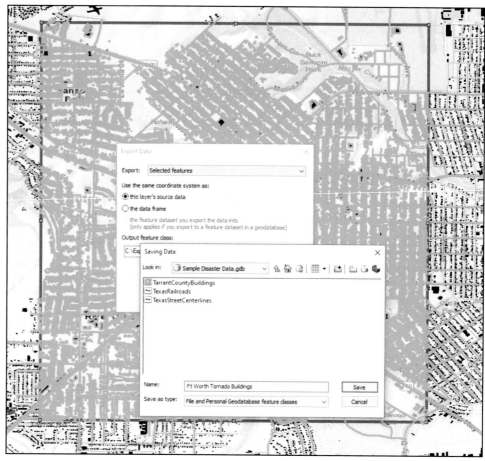

Remember that when serving data from ArcMap, ALL the layers in the map will be sent to the feature layer in AGOL – and it will try to serve any preconfigured base maps that you may have loaded. However, the process will recognize these base maps and trigger an error until you remove them from the map.

4 Right click and remove from the table of contents the Texas Railroads, Texas Street Centerlines, Tarrant County Buildings, and BaseMap layers. Then save the MXD as a new file called *Exercise 3b Buildings.mxd*.

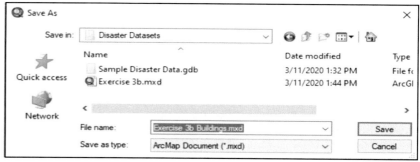

5 If your ArcMap instance is not signed in to your ArcGIS Online account, do that now.
Hint: under File select Sign In...

6 On the main menu, select File > Share As > Service.

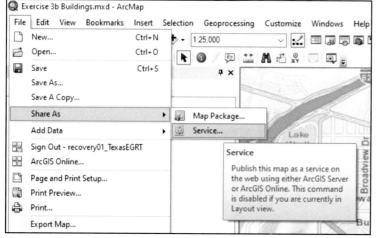

7 Select "Publish a service" and click Next.

8 In the dropdown box, select your AGOL account. Set the Service name to *Ft_Worth_Tornado_Buildings*. Then click Continue.

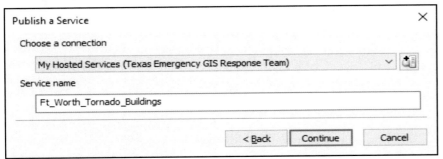

At this point you need to decide if the layer will be edited once it's in AGOL. If so, you should click on Feature Access and select the Create and Delete boxes. For this sample, this layer will not be edited.

9 Click on Item Description. Fill in the Summary and Tags, and add any other information you like to the Item Description.

The last tab is the Sharing tab. This will be covered in more detail later, but for now you can skip the Sharing settings.

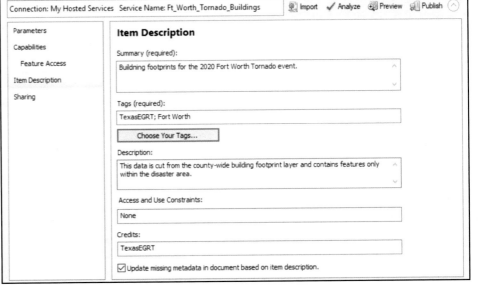

10 Click Publish. The drawing will be analyzed before publishing and produce some medium to low level errors – none of which will be a problem in AGOL since you will control symbology and scale visibility in the online maps.

That's it! But where did it wind up? When using ArcMap to serve data, you aren't prompted for a destination folder so the Feature Layer and its associated Service Definition are created in the root folder of your account. It is best if you move it into a folder specific for this disaster – and in this case the GIS Guidebooks folder.

11 Open your AGOL account (if necessary) and find the new Feature Layer and Service Definition. Click the check box next to each.

12 Just above the item list, click Move. Select the GIS Guidebooks – Disaster folder and click Move.

13 Click the GIS Guidebooks – Disaster folder in the Folders list and you will then see only the items from these exercises.

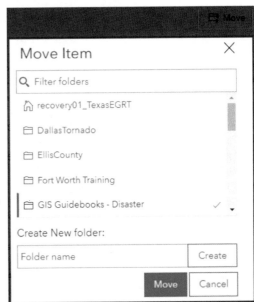

You can see that the process to share data to AGOL using ArcMap is a little tedious and has some pitfalls, but it does get the job done.

Sharing Data Through the Desktop Using ArcGIS Pro

Next you will share some data to AGOL using ArcGIS Pro. There are several advantages in using AGP over ArcMap for this. First, even if your project contains many layers you can select and share a single layer (or subset of layers) as a feature layer. Secondly, YOU CAN EDIT THE DATA DIRECTLY IN ARC GIS ONLINE USING AGP!! How cool is that! You can even change the data structure if you want, although this still may corrupt your apps. Remember that you are editing the copy of the data hosted in AGOL, not the source data, so this is still a one-way street for the most part.

Rafael's Question – I'm confused about a feature layer holding many feature layers – how does that work?

Well Esri goes a little overboard on the use of the term 'layer' and it has many different meanings in different contexts. In AGOL you will see feature layers in your Contents list. When you look at the items details of any feature layer you can see a section on the page called Layers, with a list of the data layers that are in the feature layer. Sometimes this is only one layer and sometimes this is multiple layers, depending on how the data was originally shared. When you add a feature layer to a map, or edit a feature layer in AGP, you are getting all the layers shared within that feature layer. To make things worse, the online help or tutorials (and even books like this) often use the term feature layer to mean a single layer – then turn around and use the term feature layer to mean several layers. So any time you see the term Feature Layer being used, be aware of how many layers you might be dealing with. Now prepare yourself for this news … in ArcGIS Pro the tab to create a hosted feature layer is called Web Layer.

Exercise 3C – Sharing Data Using ArcGIS Pro

In this exercise you will serve up some land base data to show property lines. This data will be both the polygons showing property ownership as well as the boundary lines of the property. This is often done so that the data can be symbolized in different ways. Since there are two layers you will want to serve up, your feature layer in AGOL will have two layers in it.

1 **Start ArcGIS Pro, if necessary, and open the project Exercise 3C.**

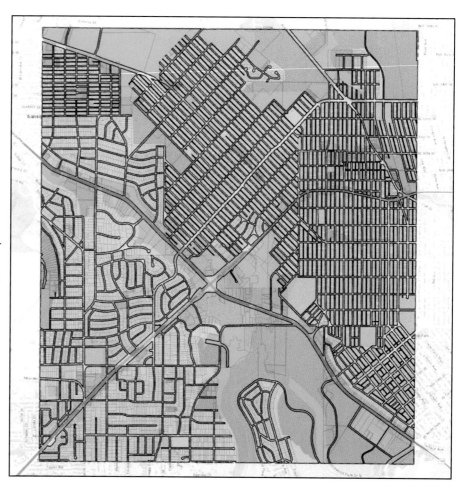

You will see data for the Ft Worth tornado event, and you will also notice the Rafael has already clipped the data for you (just to save time).

Review the list of layers in the Contents pane. The two layers that you are after are ParcelData_Clip, which contains the home owner's information, and ParcelBoundaries_Clip which is used to symbolize the property.

In AGP there are two ways to access the Share As Web Layer tool, but each way has a vastly different outcome – decide before you share data which of the two you will want to use.

Method 1 is to click the Share tab on the ribbon menu, look for the Share As tools, and click Web Layer.

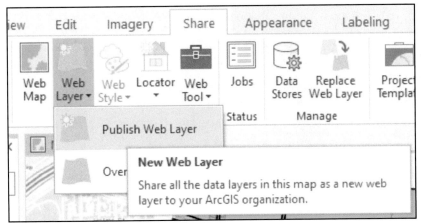

The Tool Tip tells the tale. With this method, ALL of the data layers in this project will be published into your web layer (except the base map). That's fine if you know beforehand what to expect.

Method 2 is to select the desired layers, then right click and select Sharing > Share as Web layer. Again, note the Tool Tip. Only the SELECTED layers from this project will be published.

Either method will open the same 'Share as Web Layer' dialog box! Be aware of the differences so that you don't accidently share unintended layers. Imagine accidently sharing a very large dataset – besides waiting a long time for your service to become available, your AGOL account will suddenly have a large storage burden!

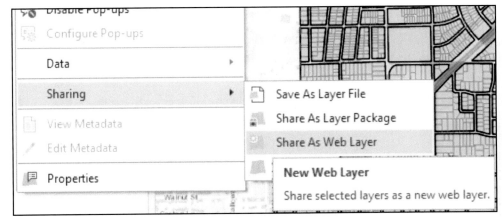

You want to use method two in this example.

2 **Highlight the two target layers in the Contents Pane.**

3 **Right-click and select Sharing > Share as Web layer.**

4 **Provide the name *FtWorthParcels* for the new shared web layer (feature layer), as well as a summary and tags.**

Note that at the bottom of the dialog you can set the sharing parameters as well as designate any Groups you would like to have access the data.

5 **Click Publish.**

When this process finishes, you will have a new hosted Feature Layer in your table of contents.

6 **Save the project and exit ArcGIS Pro.**

7 **Login to your AGOL account, if necessary, and move to the Contents tab. Select the GIS Guidebooks - Disaster folder and find the new Feature Layer. Click the Options button and select View Item Details.**

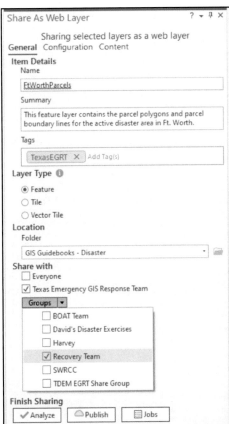

Note that the two selected layers (and only those two) were included in the feature layer. There is of course a wealth of information about these layers, and most of that has already been covered.

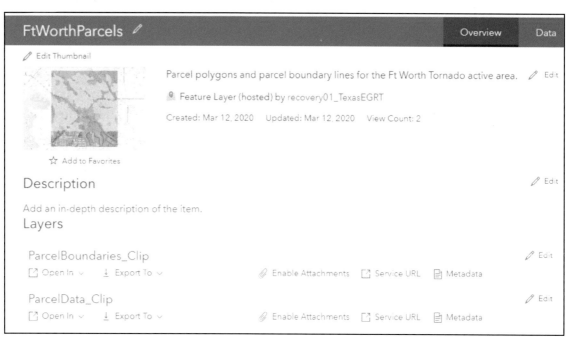

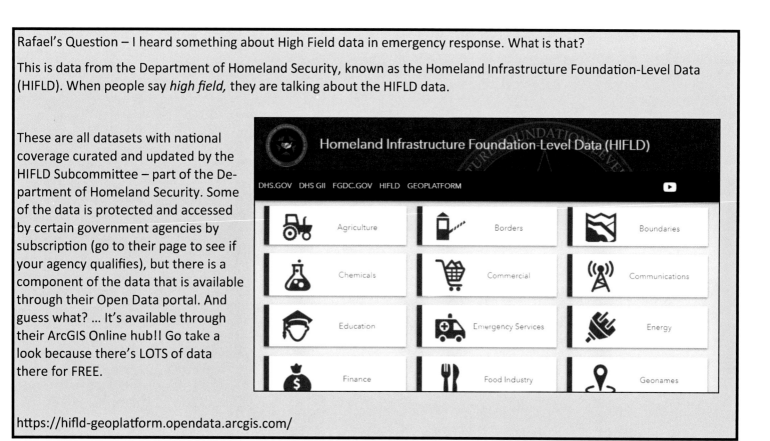

Rafael's Question – I heard something about High Field data in emergency response. What is that?

This is data from the Department of Homeland Security, known as the Homeland Infrastructure Foundation-Level Data (HIFLD). When people say *high field,* they are talking about the HIFLD data.

These are all datasets with national coverage curated and updated by the HIFLD Subcommittee – part of the Department of Homeland Security. Some of the data is protected and accessed by certain government agencies by subscription (go to their page to see if your agency qualifies), but there is a component of the data that is available through their Open Data portal. And guess what? … It's available through their ArcGIS Online hub!! Go take a look because there's LOTS of data there for FREE.

https://hifld-geoplatform.opendata.arcgis.com/

Creating and Designing New Feature Layers in ArcGIS Online

There may be a time when you need to create a totally new and empty feature layer dataset in your AGOL account, and that can certainly be done. You also have the option to use one of your existing feature layers as a temple, use a pre-designed template from Esri, or even create it on-the-fly to be total unique. As an example, you may bring in a Living Atlas dataset of major trucking routes but then want to use that as a visual guide to draw in some response zones. To do that, you would make an empty, editable feature layer with attributes that you would design yourself.

Exercise 3d – Creating New Data in ArcGIS Online

In this exercise, you are faced with the scenario where a violent storm has blown down trees and covered roads with debris. You have to map which roads are closed, then assign crews from the public works response team to different response zones. First you will first make a new feature layer from an Esri template for road closures, then add a second polygon feature marking the areas of responsibility for the public works crews you have activated. This feature layer will need to have a field for the name of the team assigned to that location, the time they were dispatched, the length of time they spent on-site (filled in after they are done), and a description of the work to be done.

1 **Start AGOL and log in to your account (if necessary). Move to the Content tab, and select the GIS Guidebooks-Disaster folder.**

2 **In the upper left, click on Create.**

You can see that there are MANY different things that can be created from this button – and as is typical with Esri software there are sometimes overlapping capabilities that you can use in different circumstances.

3 **Click Feature Layer.**

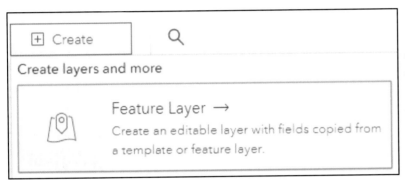

By default, the Show All category is selected and all the templates are shown. You and Rafael should look through this list and see the DOZENS of possible applications included here. Clicking on one of the templates will display a pop-up window with more information about that template before creating it.

In this instance you are looking for a specific template call Road Closures – without that knowledge you could browse by category. Knowing what templates are available may save you a lot of time in a disaster – and think outside the box because you may not find the exact template you need but find one close enough that you can modify it slightly for your unique situation.

4 **In the upper right, type Road into the search box, then click on the Road Closure image. This looks like what you want, so click Create.**

There are three feature layers that can be created with this template. If you left all three checked, you would get a feature layer with three layers in it, but you are only interested in one of them.

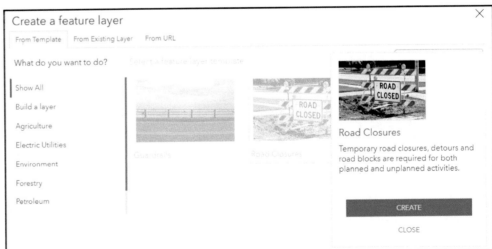

5 **Uncheck all the layers except Road Closures. Then click Next.**

Note the Capture GPS Receiver Information check box. If this is checked, a set of fields will be included to capture the longitude/latitude coordinate pair if a field device is used to create features.

Next you are asked to provide the viewable extents of the new layer. It would accept data anywhere globally, but by setting a viewable area the layer will display your target area automatically when it is added to any map.

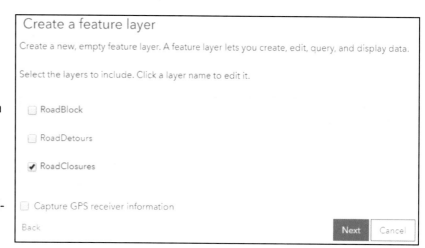

6 **Use the zoom / pan tools to zoom the map to any area of interest you like. In this example the map is zoomed to Denver. When you have set your extents click Next.**

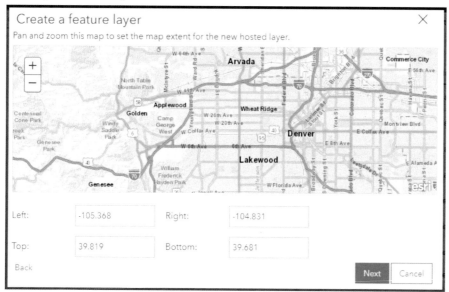

7 **Provide a title, a summary, and add any additional tags. You will see that the location has defaulted to the folder that was active when you started the creation process. When you have added your information click Done.**

Note that there was an option to assign a category to this data. You would have needed to set up a category before starting the creation process, but it is a way to have multiple layers from multiple users associated to a specific project.

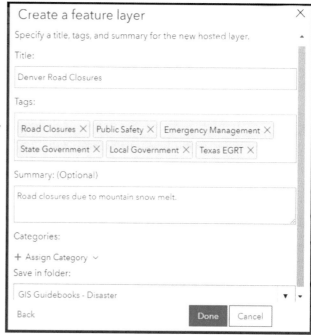

When the layer creation if finished the details page will automatically open. Here you can see all the parameters of the new layer. If you like, click on the RoadClosures layer to see all the fields that it contains. Then check Setting and you will see that it is automatically set to allow editing.

It's important to note that using this methodology the Road Closures template created a single feature layer – however the Solutions.ArcGIS.com page contains a Road Closure solution that will build all the components for a complete solution. Check out the solutions page for a detailed description, and you'll be building some of these later in this book.

The new custom feature layer is now in your Content list.

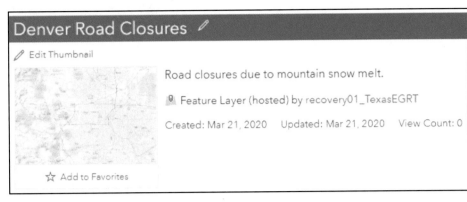

Denver Road Closures ✎

✎ Edit Thumbnail

Road closures due to mountain snow melt.

📍 Feature Layer (hosted) by recovery01_TexasEGRT

Created: Mar 21, 2020   Updated: Mar 21, 2020   View Count: 0

☆ Add to Favorites

8 **Return to the Content tab.**

Next you want to build an empty polygon into which you can draw areas of responsibility for each team that is deployed. Review the description above for the fields that will be required.

9 **Again, click the Create button and select Feature Layer.**

10 **Click the Build a Layer category on the left.**

You will see templates for the basic point, line, and polygon layers.

Note that the choice of "Point, lines, and polygons" will give you the option to create three layers, one of each type.

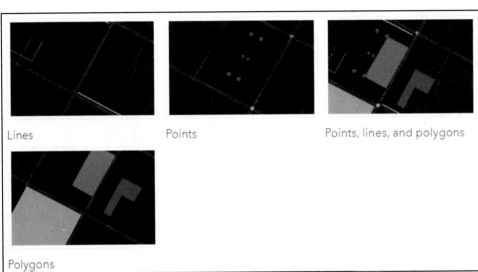

Lines

Points

Points, lines, and polygons

Polygons

11 **Select Polygons, note the description, and click Create.**

12 **Following the same steps as with the other template, set an area of interest, provide a title of *Public Works Team Assignments,* tags, and summery, then complete the layer creation.**

The new feature layer is created, added to your Content list, and set to allow editing.

Rafael's Question – Hey wait ... did I miss the part where you set up the fields?

No, you didn't miss it. These general templates only add the basic, required fields for any feature layer. In a later chapter you will set this up for use and add all the new fields.

13 **Check the Item Details for the layer, then close and log out of AGOL.**

That was a very helpful exercise to create a new, empty feature layer and the previous exercises in this chapter covered how to use ArcMap and ArcGIS Pro to put existing data into AGOL. Next you'll see how to get existing data that you might have or someone might have shared with you directly into AGOL without having to run another software.

Transferring Existing Data into ArcGIS Online

ArcGIS Online can bring in many different format files, and in fact it will accept the upload of almost any file type. Any type of desktop GIS file, such as .lyr, .mxd, .gpk, and TONS more and although these won't display in AGOL, they can be shared as downloadable files that can be opened in the desktop apps. This book, however, is focusing on feature layers or data that can be used and displayed in an AGOL map with three of the more common sources: a text file that can be geocoded, a text file that can be located with long/lat coordinates, a zipped shape file, and a zipped file geodatabase.

Exercise 3e – Importing Existing Data

In this exercise you will use different methods to bring existing data files info AGOL and create a hosted feature layer. For this scenario you have put out a request for data from all your GIS cohorts in the Dallas area to get the location of the National Guard Armories, the city limit boundaries of the region, all venues in North Texas that seat more than 5,000 people, and the locations of Dave's House of Ice (10 locations to serve you). The regional EOC is making plans for temporary shelters and they need to see what might be available. Plus the logistics team wants to investigate having the National Guard haul ice to the locations.

In a very quick time frame, you were able to get these files in the following formats (they are in the data supplied with the book):

National Guard Armory locations – comma delimited text file with address

Regional City Boundaries – zipped shape file

Dave's House of Ice locations – comma delimited text file with long/lat

North Texas Venues – zipped file geodatabase

Note: These are fake files for practice, don't use them for real life responses.

That's quite a variety of file formats, but all of those can be shared in AGOL. The easiest ones will be the zipped files, and you will start with the regional city boundaries. AGOL will consume these files in their zipped format – you won't even need to unzip them.

1 **Open ArcGIS Online and log in. Move to the Content tab and select the GIS Guidebooks – Disaster folder.**

2 **On the Content menu, click the Add Item > From your computer.**

3 **Click Choose File and navigate to the location of where you downloaded the book's datasets. Open the Exercise 3e folder and select Cities_DFW_Region.zip. Then click Open.**

Note that the Contents setting is automatically set to Shapefile.

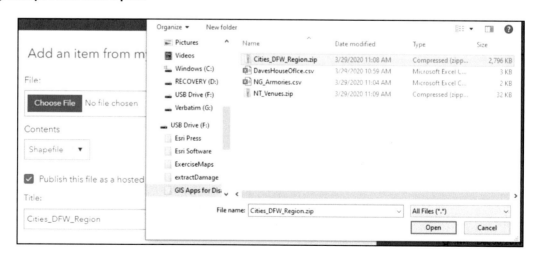

4 **You can leave the title as the default, then set some tags and assign a category if you like. When you are ready, click Add Item.**

That's it! Very simple. If you want to click on the visualization tab and see how it looks, you will notice that it is symbolized by the default single symbol.

The next file to add is the zipped file geodatabase containing the venue data.

5 **Return to the Content tab and click Add Item > From Computer.**

6 **Click Choose File and navigate to and select the file NT_Venues.zip. Click Open.**

7 **Change the Contents type to File Geodatabase using the drop down selection. Update the title to North_Texas_Large_Venues and assign tags and categories as you see fit. Click Add Item.**

Once again this was very simple. There was only one feature class in this geodatabase, but had there been more they would all have been added to the hosted feature layer.

Next you will deal with the ice house locations. These has a coordinate pair provided in longitude / latitude – and if the field names are recognized by AGOL this will also go very easily.

Rafael's Question – Why do you keep saying lat / long backwards?

In the olden days I worked for a surveyor and we provided survey data in a wide range of coordinates. Sometimes it would be in the local State Plane projection and sometimes it would be in global coordinates. As with any coordinate system, you give the coordinate values in the order of X, then Y, then Z (if applicable). For global coordinates, the X coordinate is the longitude and the Y coordinate is the Latitude – hence X,Y equals Long/Lat. My old boss would smack the back of your hand with a LeRoy lettering guide if you said it wrong.

8 **Return to the Content tab (if necessary) and click Add Item > From your computer. Click Choose File and browse to the file DavesHouseOfIce.csv. Click Open.**

9 **Provide the title *Ice_Houses* and assign a category and tags as appropriate.**

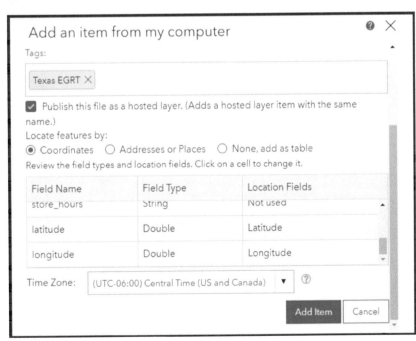

Notice that the value for 'Locate features by:' is set to Coordinates. AGOL in setting up the file for importing found two fields called Longitude and Latitude and has now prepped the input parameters to geolocate using these fields. Scroll through the Location Fields column and you will see which fields are being used. If the exact field names (or at least ones that AGOL recognizes) were not used, you could assign them manually.

10 **When everything is set, click Add Item.**

Once again this was pretty painless. Now you can add the final file – the comma delimited file with addresses.

Bringing in this file will use a process called geocoding using a locator service (if you haven't heard about that before). This process takes an address from one or more fields in the file and matches it to a street centerline file using a street name and address range for each line segment. The mechanics of geocoding is rather complex but all you need to know is the address format and the correct method for feeding it into the locator service.

11 Start the Add Item process and select the NG_Armories.csv file. Set a title, tags, and category.

12 Scroll down in the Add Item dialog and you will see that AGOL has identified this as having street addresses, and has set the import parameters … mostly.

In this instance, AGOL didn't recognize the field name containing the street address, although it did find the fields for City, State, and Zip. You need to manually set the address field.

13 In the list of fields, scroll down and find the field PHYSICAL_ADDRESS. In the Location Fields column on the same row, click Not Used and change it to Address or Place. Then click Add Item.

Once again, this was super easy – and fast!

In this case all of the addresses were successfully matched. If an address doesn't match, you will be given the chance to review the locations and hopefully you will be able to fix the data so that you get a complete match.

Your Content list now contains all of the new feature layers you have made. Note that the source files for the feature layers are also saved here. These are the CSV, File Geodatabase, and Shapefile files. They can be deleted without affecting the feature layer.

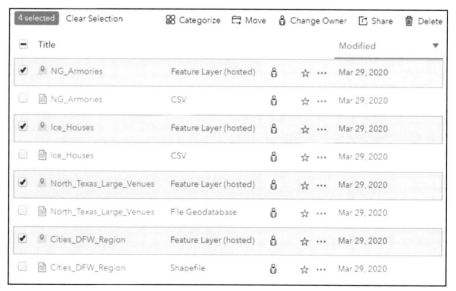

So as you see, there are lots of ways to get data into your ArcGIS Online account, including making your own empty ones. Regardless of how you accomplish this or where you get the data, it is now in a common platform and working with it will be the same.

Chapter 4 – Organizing Your Data

Rafael is anxious to get into the field structure, but before doing that it's worthwhile to take a look at ways to organize your data. It can get a little confusing with the groups, folders, categories, and tags so understanding how and why these are used will help you manage your data more efficiently.

Using Groups

A group is mostly used to determine what users can (or can't) access certain data sets. All groups are custom, and you create them in the Groups tab. From that tab, the My Groups tab will display all of the groups which have your account as a member. In this example, you can see that the current account is a member of many groups – the owner of the first two listed and a member of the second two. Down the left are different ways to filter the group list so that you could limit the display to only groups you own, only groups created within a certain time frame, and other options. You can also see the

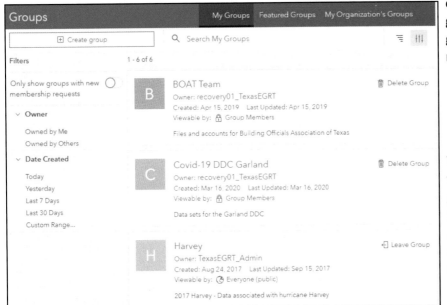

option to delete a group that you own or leave a group which has you as a member. Note that a group can't be deleted unless all members are removed from it.

Within Texas EGRT we have several groups in which all accounts are members, but certain groups with highly sensitive data, like the Covid-19 group, are restricted to just certain members … and the BOAT Team group is for accounts given to members of a specific organization that we support.

If you click on a group name (and in this case one that is owned by this account) you will see all the details of the group.

You will note that in the right-side column There is information about who can view data in this group, who can contribute items to this group, and who may update items in this group. There are also icons which display the number of members (represented by a person) and the number of items shared with this group (represented by a layer stack). Clicking the layers icon will display all of the layers that are currently shared with this group- and this page can also be reached by clicking the Content tab on the blue menu bar next to the group title. Through this page you could also add or remove layers from the group, but that can be done much more efficiently in another part of AGOL and will be discussed later. It is helpful, however, to see the items here without having to use a filter in the main contents page.

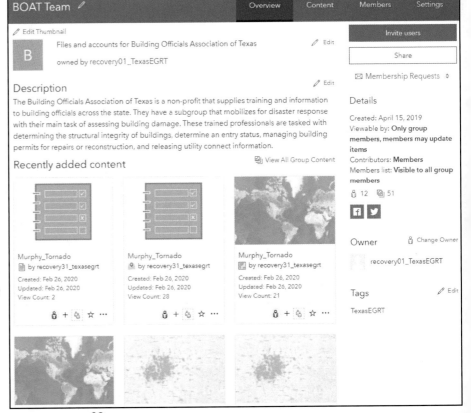

More importantly, the person icon takes you to the Group Members page – also accessible by clicking the Members tab on the blue menu bar next to the group title. This is the page where you determine who will be a member of this group.

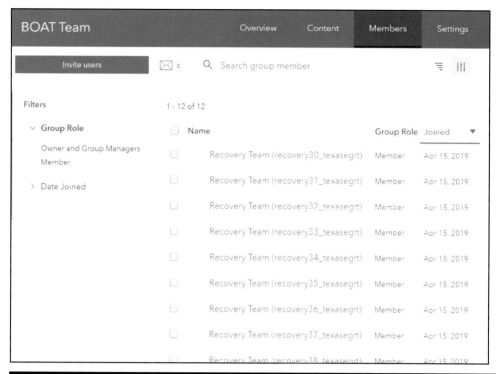

From this list you can see that the member accounts are those assigned to members of the building official's group plus the head of Tx EGRT. The eleven BOAT accounts have a unique password so if a feature layer (or ANY item) is shared with this group, they will be able to see it. If an item is shared with just this group, then ONLY THESE GROUP MEMBERS CAN SEE IT!

Rafael's Question – big deal; the BOAT team can see that data but shouldn't I be able to see it, too?

No – they may be storing (as is usually the case) a house by house assessment from tornado or flood damage and it probably contains personal or sensitive data about the property and the property owner. While it is not generally protected by law, it is a good practice to keep damage assessments private – even from other Tx EGRT members. If an unauthorized person were to access this data and either mess it up or release it to the press without authorization, you would not want to be the one who has to admit the mistake to the Incident Commander. Imaging having to ask the damage assessment team to go repeat their assessments because someone (who was not authorized) accidently deleted the data while they were making a dashboard for fun. Or what if some thieves access data you made public and come in and start looting the damaged property. Maybe you want to face that kind of heat but I sure as heck don't!

From this page you can also invite members into the group. When the Invite users button is clicked, all of the accounts in your organization that are not currently members of this group are displayed. You can check off the ones to add, then click Add to group.

Note – if you are the group owner, you can also remove members from the group. Otherwise users have to ask to be added or removed from a group.

On the image displayed before you might have noticed the Harvey group, which was used during Hurricane Harvey to manage shelter capacity and locations.

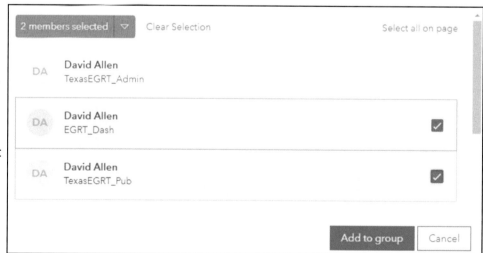

The data in that group was not only used by TxEGRT but also by many state and federal agencies, and the maps created there were used to distribute information to the public. So it was given full public access shared with everyone. The point is, determine who all will need to use the data and use that information to determine your group relationships.

Finally, at the far right of the blue Group menu, click Settings. These can control viewing and access privileges to the group as a whole.

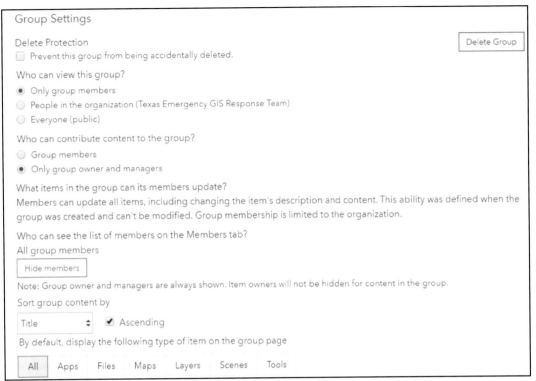

One of the most important is the Delete Protection setting. If you have given group management privileges to anyone else beside the group owner, they would be able to delete the group. Clicking the box here will prevent this – and even prevent the group owner from deleting it without specifically reviewing the settings.

The settings for 'Who can view this group' are pretty self-explanatory. Each setting from top to bottom is less restrictive. And the 'Who can contribute …' is likewise clear on its implications.

For Texas EGRT, a new group may be created for each disaster and are typically set to prevent deletion and be viewed by group members only (BOAT, however, uses the same group over and over). This offers the best security. Then the specific disaster or training exercise might determine who can contribute items to the group. In the case of the BOAT group, only the group owner or anyone designated to be a group manager can add new items or apps. This is done because the rest of the users will be doing field surveys and filling out data – not creating new items. But for other disasters the group may be set to allow any member to add items since all members working the disaster might be tasked to create datasets, apps, or dashboards at any time.

Exercise 4a – Making a Group

In this exercise you will make a group and configure the members and security. The scenario is a tornado event where about 35 structures were damaged in Rice, Texas. The Navarro County EOC has activated and they will be wanting to do a damage assessment of each structure using the local Community Emergency Response Team (CERT) members. You will want to identify four of your user accounts for this event, along with a manager account and your own account. Then build a group for this disaster and assign the user accounts to the new group. Think about what sharing settings you may want for the group, then match that with the requirements of the exercise later.

1 Start AGOL and login (if necessary). Click the Groups tab.

2 At the top of the screen, click Create group.

3 Add a Group Name, Summary, and Tags as necessary.

It would be really impressive to add the CERT logo to this group, indicating that they will be performing the required work. The CERT logo is a jpeg format is included in the data distributed with this book.

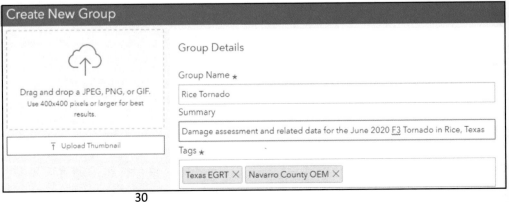

4 Using the File Explorer window, navigate to the folder where you stored the data distributed with this book. Drag the CERT_Logo.jpg file into the thumbnail box. Ten set the zoom slider so that the entire logo is visible and click OK.

What did you decide about this group's viewability and membership? Would it help to know that the same storm produced a tornado in Mildred (same county) and you'll be setting up a similar group with designated accounts for the Mildred Volunteer Fire Department? You will want these two groups to be a secure as possible, and neither group will need to see the data from the other group. However, the account that is assigned to the Navarro OEM will need access to both groups.

With that information in hand, the settings will be:

Who can view this group?

Only group members. We don't want people who are not working a specific disaster to see the data, or have them get confused by seeing data from other disasters.

Who can contribute content to this group?

Only group owner and managers. We want to minimize the chance of adding extraneous data to the group.

What items in the group can its members update?

All items. The fields crews will be using a mobile app and need to be able to have their collected data added to the feature layers.

Who can see the list of members?

Doesn't matter ... most won't have access to that screen or know what it represents. Nor will they have any permissions to alter the list.

5 Make the appropriate setting and click Create Group.

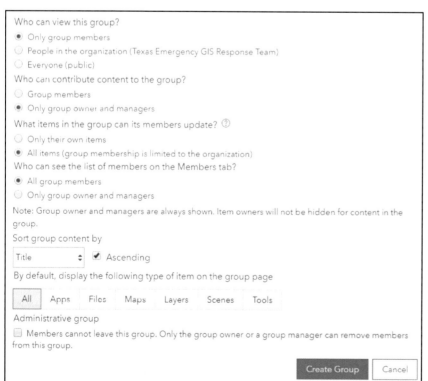

With the group created, you will need to add members to the group. For this exercise you will see many of the Texas EGRT accounts, and your AGOL account will have different users. You can decide which of your accounts you would like to add to the group.

We are going to have the account for the head of Texas EGRT in this group (and who is the group creator), and use the account recovery20_TexasEGRT for the Navarro County Emergency Management Coordinator. Then we will add accounts recover21 through recovery25 for the five field teams to use. Note – the administrator typically resets the passwords to the assigned accounts at each disaster and that information is shared only with the response teams on the event.

6 Click the Invite Users button.

7 Scroll down and select the users you wish to add (your member accounts will differ). Note the option to add members without requiring confirmation, which is desired. Click Add to Group.

Next you need to make recovery20 a group manager so that they can have more control over the items and members in the group. This is done from the Members list in the group page.

8 Click the Members tab on the blue Group menu (if necessary) to see the accounts. Check the box next to the user account recovery20_TexasEGRT. Just above the member list, click the Update Member's Group Role button.

9 Change the role to Group Manager and click Update.

10 Click the Setting tab, review your choices, and turn on the Delete Protection.

11 Return to the main Groups tab and you will see your new group listed with the rest, including the CERT logo.

The important lesson here was how to create a group for a disaster, then control who has access to the group and what their privileges are. In the olden days (last year) we would set almost all data as public because it was easier for all involved if they didn't have to deal with passwords. Then we had some data breaches during a disaster which brought to light the issues with making all your data public, and new operating protocols for data protection were implemented. Our partner agencies are much happier with our level of security, and once you understand and practice the processes for making these various items it isn't that much additional work.

As you can see, the Group structure is a great way to add some security to your data.

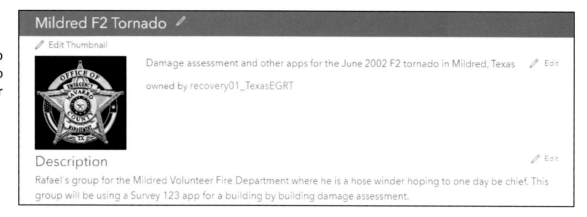

Mildred F2 Tornado ✎

✎ Edit Thumbnail

Damage assessment and other apps for the June 2002 F2 tornado in Mildred, Texas   ✎ Edit

owned by recovery01_TexasEGRT

Description   ✎ Edit

Rafael's group for the Mildred Volunteer Fire Department where he is a hose winder hoping to one day be chief. This group will be using a Survey 123 app for a building by building damage assessment.

Tagging and Categorizing Your Data

Now you will look at some ways in which to add designations to your data and make it easier to find in the sometimes-long Gallery or Contents lists.

First are tags. You've already seen how tags are added to items both when you were making and adding layers to your account, but also when you created a group. Tags are both an internal and external organizing feature and are used when searching for data. They typically identify the agency, the type of data, and key words about the content. Keep in mind, too, that user's search statements look at these tags but also consider the item's title, summary, and description. For instance, the City of Austin water utility department might have this information on a layer:

Tags: "City of Austin", "Water Utility", "Meter Locations", and "Municipal Water Supply"

Title: – High Usage Water Meters

Summary: Seven Day Residential Water Usage Analysis

Description: Summary analysis of residential water meter readings over a seven day period to locate meters using water above the expected average. The analysis uses the constant read, wi-fi enabled meters and reports that total water usage in 12 hour increments.

Anyone in the world (if the data was shared as public) or within your organization could enter search keywords and if they appeared in a layer's tags, title, summary, or description the layer would be found and shown in the search results. There are thousands of possible searches that would return this layer. But for this to work correctly and be of some benefit, you need to be diligent about making the information in these components comprehensive and descriptive. Imagine a layer with this documentation set:

Tags: "City of Blue Rock", "Public Works"

Title: Blue Rock Public Works

Summary: Blue Rock Public Works Department Map

Description: Map of the City of Blue Rock Public Works Utility"

In total there's about 5 searches that could be done here – and yes you would probably find this with a search on Blue Rock (along with a thousand other matches that you could wade through) but find nothing if you looked for "Residential Water Usage" or "Wi-fi enabled meters".

For Texas EGRT it is common to use the tag "Texas EGRT" and the name of the disaster that the data pertains to, such as "Mildred Tornado". If the data is brought in from another agency, it is suggested that you add that agency's name to the Tags list. For instance, if you brought in the HIFLD data for railroads the tags might include "HIFLD Open Data".

Then we rely on the title, summary, and description to contain more detailed information and keywords. It's easy to go nuts with tags – you can put as many as you like at no extra charge, and in some situations the software will add tags for you automatically (read the help for more information on this). Just remember that these components all work together to create a solid and effective basis for searches, so if you want to go nuts on something do it on the description.

Another organizing tool is using Categories. These are INTERNAL markers letting you identify data by not only the owner or source, but by the topic of the data. Some of the standard category sets come from Esri, the International Organization for Standardization, or INSPIRE (a European standards group). The lists can be found in the ArcGIS help and include topics such as Basemaps, People, Infrastructure, Environment, Boundaries, farming and many more. The categories can also have sub-categories which can give more detail within a certain topic. For instance, the Environment category has sub-categories of Oceans, Earth, Weather, Energy, and more. When you visit the Living Atlas or HIFLD data hubs you are presented with these categories in the browse menu.

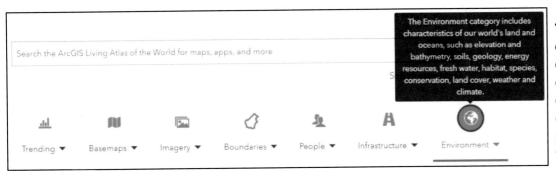

You can also define your own categories and sub-categories. It is recommended that you use the standard categories for your data except where here is no appropriate category or you need to identify it differently.

As an example, you might build a category of Infrastructure in your organization that matches the Living Atlas, but also have a more specialized category or data you create yourself.

In Texas EGRT we are not using categories to their fullest yet but the next exercise will demonstrate how to create them, and perhaps lend more ideas on how to best implement this feature.

Exercise 4b – Setting Up Categories

In this exercise you will be setting up some categories that you can use with your response data. First you can set some up using the Esri standards. Then you can set up some custom categories that are specific to disasters.

1 Open ArcGIS Online and log in (if necessary).

2 Go to the Content tab. In the left column look for the title Categories. Click the down arrow to expand the list.

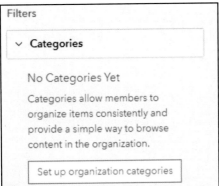

You'll see that no categories have been set up yet. If your organization already had categories set up, you can skip down a bit and work on custom categories.

3 Click on the Set Up Organizational categories button.

There are three sets of standard categories, as mentioned above. Each has an information button that when clicked will open a new webpage with details on the categories for that group.

4 Highlight the ArcGIS Categories. You have the option to remove any category that you do not want to add, but in this example you will take them all. Click Save.

Now the list should contain all of the categories from the ArcGIS list. That will cover a lot of themes and topics, and now you will want a category for Disasters with a sub-category for each of the types of disasters that you may respond to.

As an example, you will make a new category called Disaster Data, then make a sub-category for Tornado, Flood, Wildfire, Pandemic, Hurricane, and Riot.

Avoid making a category called "Other" as a catch-all. If it's important enough to warrant a disaster response then it's important enough to have a category.

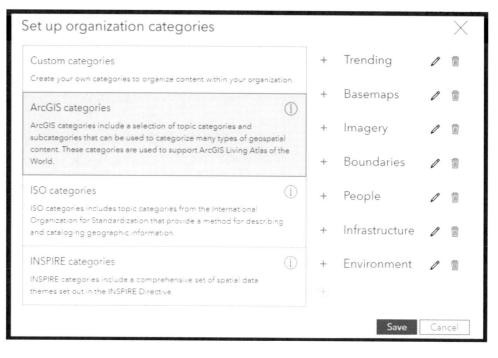

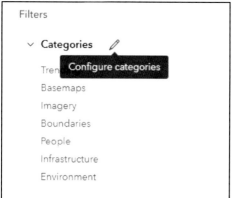

5 Click the Edit (pencil icon) next to the Categories title to open the configuration page.

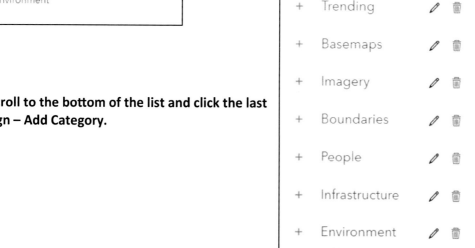

6 Scroll to the bottom of the list and click the last plus Sign – Add Category.

7 Type in the category name Disaster Data and click Save.

8 Then click the plus sign below the new name to add a sub-category.

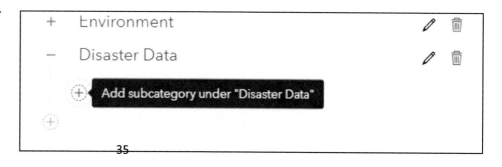

9 Type in the sub-category name of Tornado and click Save.

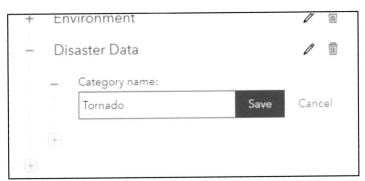

That's pretty simple. And notice that you can add a sub-sub-category.

The only issue here is that you have to design out your category strategy and build it first before you can set a category for any data. If you wait until you have hundreds of datasets before implementing categories the task will be more laborious.

10 Add the other sub-categories for the Disaster main category.

This worked so well that maybe we'll start adding a subcategory with each disaster name.

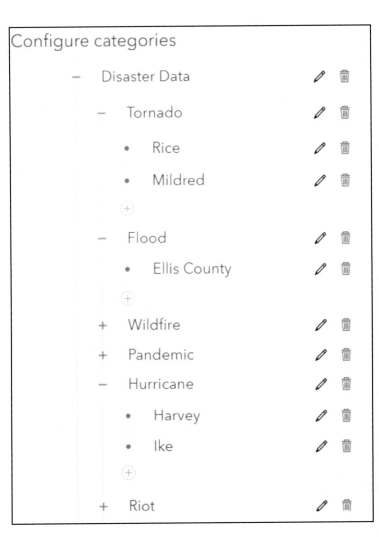

11 Click the X in the upper right to close out the category configuration dialog.

12 If you are not continuing, log out and close AGOL.

The last organizing feature is the use of folders, which you did earlier on. By using all of these methods in conjunction with each other you can build a pretty strong library of data that will produce relevant searches and fast ways to locate your data.

Chapter 5 – Setting Up Web Data for Use

Now that you've seen how to get data from various online sources, your own computer, and even create new feature layers it's time to see how to set them up to be organized and consumed in your maps and apps (before Raffy has a fit).

Layer Details

In chapter 3 you created a feature layer called Public Works Team Assignments using the generic polygon template. This feature layer will need to have fields added for the name of the team assigned to that location, the time they were dispatched, the length of time they spent on-site (filled in after they are done), and a description of the work to be done. You also created a feature layer called Denver Road Closures using a preset solutions template. You will start by looking at the road closure feature layer, then using that knowledge to prepare the team assignments layer for use.

Open ArcGIS Online and go to the Content tab (if necessary). Click on the GIS Guidebooks – Disaster folder.

Click on the Denver Road Closures (or click Options and select View Item Details).

You will be default be on the Overview tab of the layer. There are four other tabs - Data, Visualization, Usage, and Settings, each controlling certain aspects of the layer.

The Overview tab shows the layer name, description terms of use, and other information that you may have defined when you created the layer. Each can be edited, and as you saw before these have an impact on any data searches you do. The Overview tab even has an Item Information slider letting you know the strength of your metadata. In this instance, the layer rates rather highly after more metadata was added, although the meter is suggesting a longer description. This is subjective, although a longer description would increase the number of possible search combinations that could find this data.

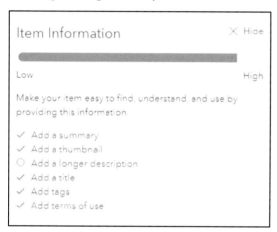

In the lower right of the display is a column displaying much of the technical information about the layer, such as the source, latest update, owner, storage folder, categories, tags, and credits.

The last thing listed is pretty important if you have others that want to use this layer – the URL to the data service. If you send this to anyone else, and they have the correct permissions, they can use the layer in any of their maps.

You saw earlier how to add a layer using the URL – well this is where the URL comes from. Just click the Copy button and paste it into messages, documents e-mails, or whatever you like.

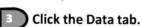 Click the Data tab.

The default screen shows the records in the layer – this layer doesn't have any yet. Clicking on any field will show some actions you can take on the field including sorting, calculating, or even deleting.

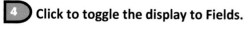

If the layer is set to be editable, you could edit the data in this table.

In the upper right of the display is a toggle button to change to the field view of the data.

 Click to toggle the display to Fields.

This displays all the fields and their type, and adds the ability to add new fields.

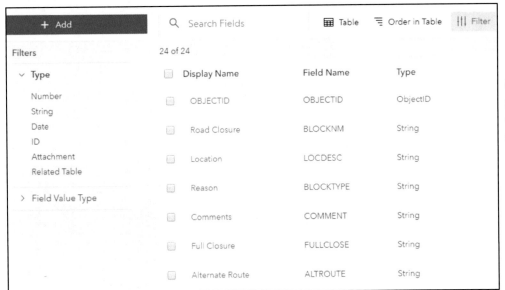

Clicking on any field name will display more information about the field, and you will see more about that later in this chapter.

5 Click on the field Full Closure. Note all the parameters for this field, and notice that it has a section at the bottom called List of Values (Domain).

The value list works exactly like the domains in ArcGIS – that is it restricts the entries of this field to only those values expressed on this list. There is an edit icon next to the list that will open a box and allow you to enter additional values. That might not be appropriate for this field, but perhaps you should add more values to the Reason field. That field has some generic values but more specific ones might be more appropriate in a disaster. You will add some values for 'Disaster – Flood', 'Disaster – Damaged', 'Disaster – Debris Blockage', and 'Disaster – Restricted Access'.

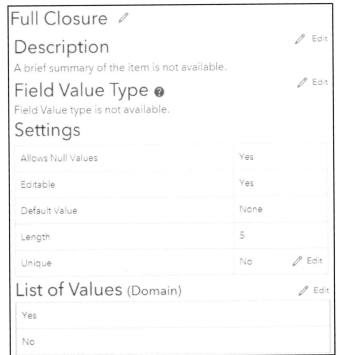

6 Click the Reason field. Note that it also has a list with existing values. Click the Edit icon next to the list.

7 In the new window, click +Add at the bottom and add the label *Disaster – Flood* with a code of *Flood.*

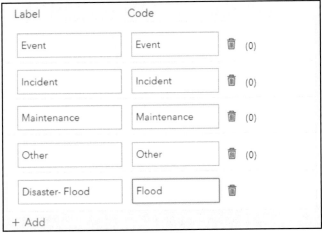

8 Click Add and add the three additional values listed above.
9 When completed, click Save.

You can add as many choices as are practical, but probably keep it under 10. Too many and it becomes a chore to scroll through the list when entering data. Notice also that each value has a display next to it showing how many features in the data have used that value. This is helpful if you want to remove a choice from the list – you would then know how many features no longer conform to your domain. Note that if you delete a value from the list, it doesn't alter the existing data, this would only have an effect on future data that is added.

10 Click the Visualization tab.

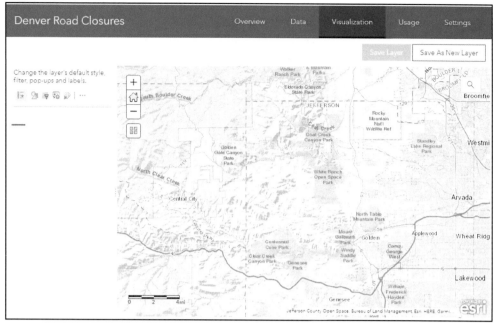

This is a very powerful tab for setting up a layer in that it allows you to design the style and/or data classification for the layer; set filters on the data; configure the pop-up window, make labels, and MUCH MORE.

In fact, ALL of the characteristics of a layer that you can design in the Map Viewer can be done here.

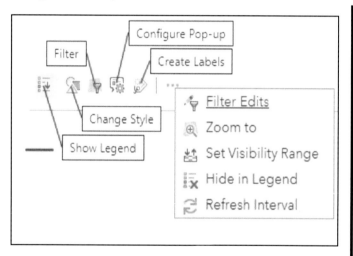

Rafael's Question – Why would I want to set all this up here when I can set it up in the map viewer?

If you set all this up here in the layer details pane and save it, then it will be the default configuration every time you add this layer to a new map. Image having a land use polygon layer which has an industry standard color scheme that is always used, and it has a lot of categories and a lot of different colors. Add to that the fact that the layer would be used in dozens of maps. If you set it up here and save it, then you would never have to set all the categories and colors again. However, if you had a feature layer with a variety of interesting data fields in it (like a Census dataset) then you might not set the symbol styles here but allow it to be set independently in each map you might create.

11 If you aren't continuing, log out and close AGOL.

Setting Symbology in ArcGIS Online

In this next exercise you'll first look at how the visualization parameters are set up for the Road Closures layer then set up some of these parameters for the team assignments layer. Later on you will work with more of the settings using the Map Viewer. Here's the interesting part – if you set all of this up in the Map Viewer you can optionally save your setting back to the layer and next time you come back to the Visualization screen you will see the new settings. OR you can make changes in the Map Viewer but NOT save them back to the layer and the settings in the Visualization screen won't change. For example, maybe you add the pre-symbolized land use layer to your map and you want to specifically highlight vacant land using a filter or a different color. That set-up would only display in that particular map and would not overwrite the original settings of the feature layer. Later if you added the land use layer to another map you'd get the standard land use classification you had set up earlier.

First a quick word on terminology. When working in ArcGIS Pro you set the appearance of your data using the terms Symbology and Classification. In AGOL you set the appearance of your data using the terms visualization and styles. They mean the same thing and work pretty much the same way, and this exercise will use the AGOL terms.

In the previous exercise you added some values to a pick list for the field Reason, and now you want to color code the roads according to that list. There were sone items in the list from the default layer, and you can color them differently because they are not involved in the disaster.

For this layer, a nice set of symbols might be:

Disaster – Flood : Thick blue line

Disaster – Damaged: Thick red line

Disaster – Debris Blockage: Thick orange line

Disaster – Restricted Access: Medium thickness red dashed line.

All others: Medium thickness dark purple line

This can be set with the layer as the default, then if you use it in a different type of map later you can always override this color scheme.

1 **Open ArcGIS Online and find the GIS Guidebooks – Disaster folder. Locate the Denver Road Closures layer and open the item details (if necessary).**

2 **Move to the Visualization tab.**

You can see that the layer is currently symbolized with everything shown with a red line.

Change the layer's default style, filter, pop-ups and labels.

Change Style

3 **Click the Change Style button.**

4 **Click the drop down list under 'Choose an attribute to show' and select Reason. You will get a warning about changing the types of features you can create and you can click Yes.**

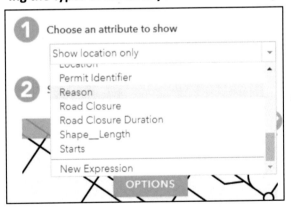

A default set of symbols is displayed but you will change those.

5 **Under 'Select a drawing style' click Options.**

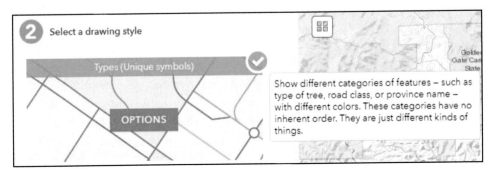

Select a drawing style

Types (Unique symbols)

OPTIONS

Show different categories of features – such as type of tree, road class, or province name – with different colors. These categories have no inherent order. They are just different kinds of things.

At the bottom of the list you will see two lines labeled Other. The next to last instance of Other is one of the values in the pick list for the field Reason. That bottom instance, however, is something special within this dialog. It is a group symbol called Other that allows you to take several of the values and group them into a single symbol. Then you can set a single symbol for all the items in the group, and even control the visibility with the check box. You are going to do this with the non-disaster related values. There's only one of these group items (unlike in Pro) so use it wisely. Items are moved by grabbing the three vertical dots at the left of their name and sliding them up or down. A dashed blue line will show where the item will drop if released.

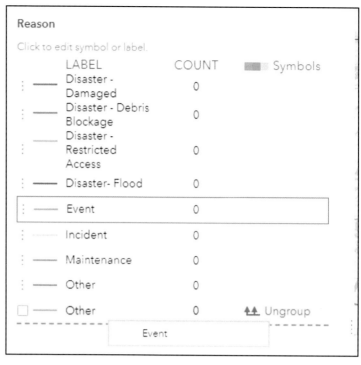

6 Click the dots to the left of the value **Event** and drag it down into the **Other** group and release it.

7 Repeat with the values **Incident, Maintenance, and Other. Check the box so that these values will be shown.**

The rest of the values will be symbolized according to the list shown earlier. This is done by clicking the symbol in the list, then managing various setting in the symbol creation box.

8 Click the symbol next to the value **Disaster- Damaged. This will be shown as a thick red line.**

9 The line is already using red, so move down and change the width to 4. This can be done either by clicking the in the value box for Line Width and typing 4, or by dragging the slider bar over to 4. Click OK to finish.

10 Next, click on the symbol for **Disaster – Restricted Access.** Again, the color is already red so change the thickness to 4.

11 Click the drop down list for **Pattern and select the third choice – the medium dashed line. Click OK to finish.**

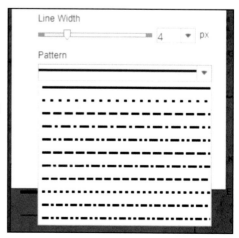

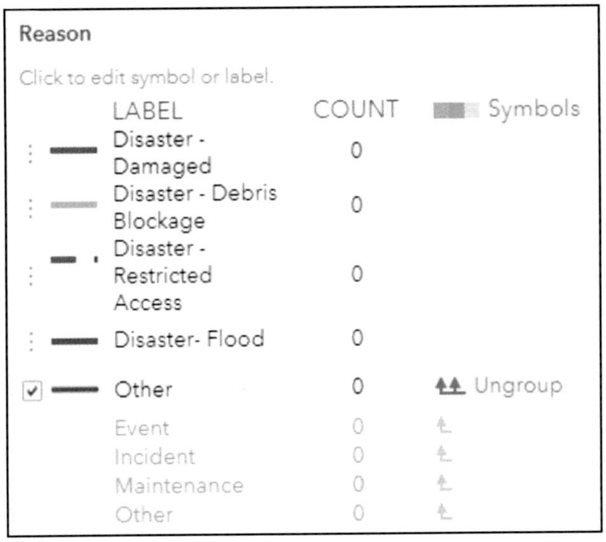

Reason
Click to edit symbol or label.
LABEL
COUNT
Symbols
Disaster - Damaged
0
Disaster - Debris Blockage
0
Disaster - Restricted Access
0
Disaster- Flood
0
Other
0
Ungroup
Event
0
Incident
0
Maintenance
0
Other
0

Rafael's Challenge – The last three steps involve changing the color and setting an appropriate line thickness for a style. See if you can do the changes shown here on your own.

Hint – it's the same process as step 9 above with the addition of selecting a color.

12 Click OK then Done when all the settings are completed.

Note that you can remove any or all of the items in the Other group at any time and set the symbol separately.

In the symbol editing box you may have noticed a button in the upper right called 'Symbol'. This will let you apply symbol formatting to all of the symbols at once. For instance, if you had 20 values and you wanted them all to be dashed, you could use this option to change them all at once. You could even set up a color ramp for all the values.

13 In the upper right, click the Save layer button. This will store all of your new settings.

Because these style changes were saved with the layer, they are now the default styles that will be used every time this layer is placed into a map. Pre-setting the styles is very useful if the data is to be shown in several maps and you want continuity in the styles, or if you are using an industry standard color scheme such as land use or zoning. Remember that you can always change the style once the layer is in a map without changing the default styles.

14 If you are not continuing, log out and close AGOL.

Working with Templates

Earlier you made a new feature layer called Public Works Team Assignments. It was made with a default empty polygon template, and now needs to be set up for use. If you recall, the layer needed to have a field for the name of the team assigned to that location, the time they were dispatched, the length of time they spent on-site (filled in after they are done), and a description of the work to be done. For the team name, you can set up a value list of Team 1 through team 10. For the description, it can also be a value list for the four things they might be doing; Clearing a road, setting up barricades, inspecting the damage, or controlling traffic. Next you can set up the visualization for the layer (shades of red and orange based on the work being done) and finally the sharing.

Exercise 5c – Configuring a Blank Template Layer

The first part of configuring this layer will be to add the fields and value lists described above.

1 Open AGOL and go to the Contents tab (if necessary). Locate the Public Works Team Assignments feature layer and open the item details.

The Item Information gauge displayed on the right side of the screen is at about 50%, and you should make that higher so that you can increase the search capabilities. The best way to do that is to fill out a good summary, description and terms of use.

2 Using the edit button for each, add more verbiage to the summary, description, and terms of use. This is only an exercise so you can be inventive. Be sure to save changes and check the Information gauge.

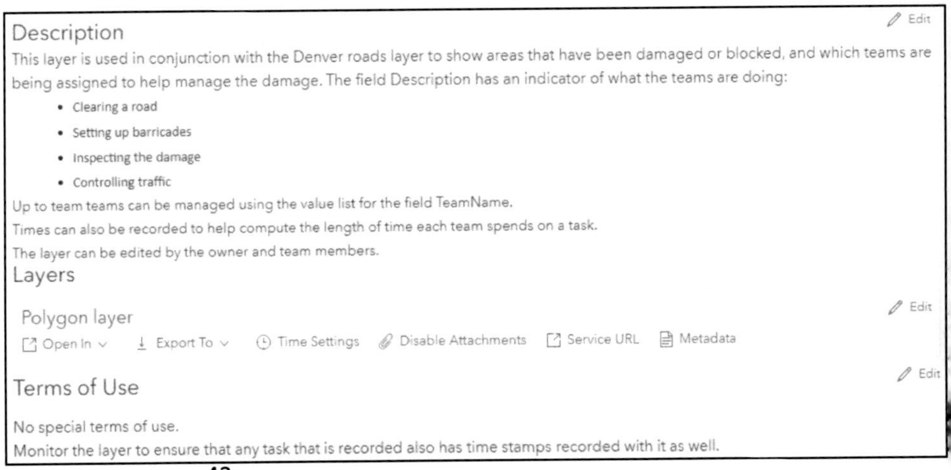

Description
Edit
This layer is used in conjunction with the Denver roads layer to show areas that have been damaged or blocked, and which teams are being assigned to help manage the damage. The field Description has an indicator of what the teams are doing:
Clearing a road
Setting up barricades
Inspecting the damage
Controlling traffic
Up to team teams can be managed using the value list for the field TeamName.
Times can also be recorded to help compute the length of time each team spends on a task.
The layer can be edited by the owner and team members.
Layers
Polygon layer
Edit
Open In
Export To
Time Settings
Disable Attachments
Service URL
Metadata
Terms of Use
Edit
No special terms of use.
Monitor the layer to ensure that any task that is recorded also has time stamps recorded with it as well.

Next you need to add four fields – one for the team names; one for the dispatch time; one for the time spent on the job, and one for the job description. Remember that the team name and job description fields will have a value pick list.

3 Move to the Data tab and click the Fields button.

4 Next click the Add button. Provide the field name of TeamName with a display name of Team Name. Uncheck the Allow Null Values box. When completed, click Add New Field.

5 Now add a field for DispatchTime with a field type of Date. Click Add New Field when done.

6 Add the next two fields on your own: Elapsed Time as a double and JobDesc as text.

The last part of this is to add a value list to two of the fields, which you've done in an earlier exercise. See if you can complete that on your own first – but a hint is given as an outline in the next step.

7 Click the field name, then click Create list. Add each value and type in both a Label and a Code for each value. Be sure to save the lists when done.

Now you can set the visualization. This will be done using the Job Description field, and to make things easy you can select any color ramp you like. Again, see if you can complete this, or use the hint in the next step.

8 Go to the Visualization tab. Click the Change Style button. Set the attribute to Job Description, then click Options and change the color ramp. Click OK and Done to finish. Finish by saving the layer.

That completes the layer set-up and it is now ready to share and use.

Just as you were finishing this, the boss came in with another request concerning this layer. They would like to be able to display this data in a non-editable form and show the status of each current job. They will use Arcade scripts to display only active jobs and how long each job is taking. That part won't concern you but you will need to make a non-editable view of this layer.

9 On the right column of the Overview tab, click Create View Layer.

10 Name the new layer *Active Public Works Jobs*. Accept the rest of the default values and click OK.

11 When the new view is created, the Item Details page for that layer is opened. Add a description and other metadata.

12 If you are not continuing, exit ArcGIS Online.

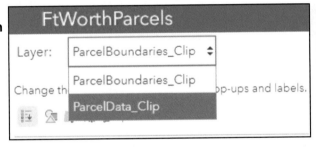

Create View Layer ✕

Create a new view of this feature layer that references the same data, yet allows you to independently set how it's shared with others, how it's drawn, what features are displayed (filtering) and whether it can be edited.

Title:

Active Public Works Jobs

That was quite a bit of work to set these layers up, and all of the setting will be highly valuable when the layer is put into use. Remember that you should set up as much as possible BEFORE the layer goes into use because changing it afterwards can be very difficult. For instance, if you were to later define a new job description and add it to the value list, all of the users that have this layer open in an app would need to refresh the app to see the list additions. If some don't refresh, then they might not be getting current data.

Symbology for Polygon Layers

Before doing too much more with the fields and tables, Rafael wants to try setting the visualization for a polygon layer to see how that is different. Remember earlier you made a parcel dataset for Ft Worth, and it has a field for Age of Structure. You will symbolize that using a green scale with the newer parcels being a darker green.

Exercise 5d – Setting the Visualization for Polygons

1 If you closed your AGOL account after the previous exercise, open it again and return to the GIS Guidebooks – Disaster folder. Find the FtWorthParcels layer and open the item details. Recall that this feature layer actually has two datasets in it, one for the parcels and one for the parcel outlines.

2 Click the Visualization tab. In the upper left, click the drop down list for layers and select ParcelData_Clip.

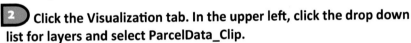

FtWorthParcels

Layer: ParcelBoundaries_Clip ⬍
ParcelBoundaries_Clip
Change th___ op-ups and labels.
ParcelData_Clip

This will change the display to the other layer, but it will prompt you to save the changes to the boundaries layer. You get this because the layer had no symbols set before, and a default set was made when you opened the visualization tab.

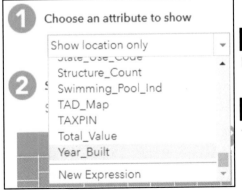

Choose an attribute to show

Show location only ▼

State_Use_Code
Structure_Count
Swimming_Pool_Ind
TAD_Map
TAXPIN
Total_Value
Year_Built

New Expression ▼

3 When prompted, click Yes to save the default symbols for the boundaries layer.

4 Click the Change Style button and change the "Choose attribute …" selection to Year_Built. Answer Yes to the warning.

The result is not what was expected. It's showing the year as text, which means it can either show a single symbol for everything or a unique value for each text value. That display is garbage! AGOL can only show a limited number of unique values and all the rest are in the Other group. You could never discern the age of a structure if every value from 1800 to 2020 is a unique color – you want there to be a graduated range of colors. What a mess. Why did Rafael want to do this in the first place? But hey, maybe there's a way you can bail him out.

The problem is that the field is formatted as text, even though it contains a four digit integer. If you can reform the value into a number with four digits then AGOL will let you symbolize it as graduated colors. You will do this with a simple Arcade expression.

** There's not enough room in this book to go over all of what Arcade can do, but if you check the GIS Guidebooks.com website you will find that Rafael and I already wrote a whole book on that! **

The Arcade function to use is called Number. It wants the field name and some code to show the format of the output value. A pound sign (or hashtag for you kids) represent a digit, so you will use "####". Note that this could include commas, dollar signs, and decimal places if you were formatting something like money, but for year you don't typically show those things. (Money would be "$###,###,###.##" for amounts up to the hundreds of millions)

5 **Click the "Choose and attribute …" again and this time select New Expression. An expression builder box will open.**

6 **Write the expression Number($feature["Year_Built"], "####") and click Test. If there is an error, double check the expression.**

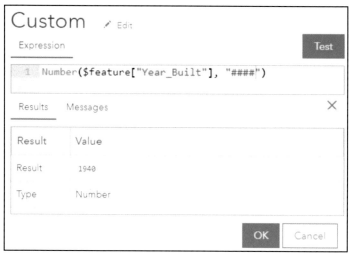

One little detail that is important to do is to change the name of the expression. By default this was called 'Custom' and that's what will display in the legend and in any reference to this value. Not very descriptive, so you will change it.

7 **Click the Edit button next to Custom and change to 'Year of Construction' and click Save.**

8 **Click OK to continue.**

Now the choices for visualization will include Counts and Amounts (Size), which equates to Graduated Symbol in Pro; and Counts and Amounts (Color), which equates to Graduated Colors in Pro. Note the check mark showing that the style Counts and Amounts is currently being used, but the different sized dots are not appropriate here.

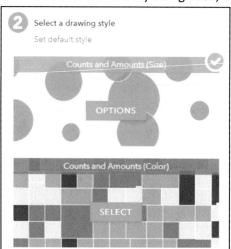

9 **Select Counts and Amounts (Color). Note that the check mark moved and the display is now shown in shades of color rather than dots. Click Options and click the Classify Data box.**

This is a very intimidating looking interface because it has a LOT of functionality built into a small space. If you take it slow and go one step at a time you can easily get through this.

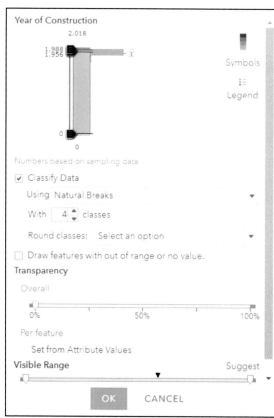

The default has set the visualization to 4 class using the Jenks Natural Breaks classification. The numbers are shown from 0 to 2018 – but in actuality the lowest recorded year in this area is 1900. Everything with a number of 0 is showing that the year of construction isn't known. With that information you know that you will want to show everything from 0 to 1900 as "Year Not Known" and the rest of the data classified into groups – and Rafael suggests 20 year gaps from 1900 to 2020. That would be 7 classes. With some work this can be achieved.

45

First will be to set the color range to a light to dark gradation.

10 **In the upper right of the pane click on Symbols. Select the light-to-dark green panel and click OK.**

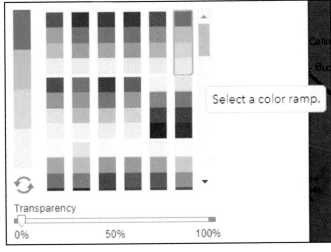

Select a color ramp.

Transparency

0% 50% 100%

Next will be to tackle the number of classes. When you look at the vertical scale showing the values, the range from 0 to 1900 is so large that the remaining ranges are shown in an overlapping group at the top. You can temporarily change the appearance of this to make it easier to set, then change back to the full range of number when you are done. The way to do this is to change the bottom number from o to 1890. Then set all the other values – and finish by setting the bottom value back to 0.

11 **Change the number of classes to 7. Then click the number 0 on the left of the scale (not the one below it) and change it to 1900. Next click the 0 below the scale and change it to 1900 as well.**

12 **Now click each of the numbers at the left of the scale, starting from bottom to top, and set them from 1900 to 2000 in 20 year increments.**

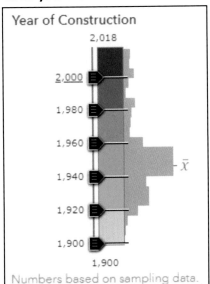

Year of Construction
2,018
2,000
1,980
1,960
$\bar{x}$
1,940
1,920
1,900
1,900
Numbers based on sampling data.

What interesting is that a grey histogram is shown to the right of the scale ad you can see that this area of Ft. Worth had a building boom in the 1940's.

13 **When all your values are set, change the number below the scale back to 0.**

In the map display you can see a preview of the legend. The ranges look fine, except that you want to change the bottom range to "Year Not Known".

14 **In the upper right of the pane, click on the Legend button. Highlight the last row and type in "Age Not Know" and press Enter. Also, take the comma's out of the year values since these aren't commonly used when showing years.**

You can adjust the transparency, the color, or the visible scale range without altering the classifications you set.

15 **If you are happy with the finished results, click OK and Done. Then click Save layer to save this style set-up.**

Rafael's Challenge – showing the color scale by year brought up an interesting point, and Rafael wants to make a new layer to use in another project. It was noted that this area of Ft. Worth had a building boom in the 1940's so Rafael wants to show the regular green gradations you set up, except color the scale from 1940 to 1960 in a dark orange so that it will stand out. Can you figure out how to do this?

Hint: Go back into the Change Style Options, click the Legend button, and click on the color next to the 1940 to 1960 range. Set it to a new color, then OK and Done.

If you succeed, click Save As New Layer and call it Fort Worth Building Boom.

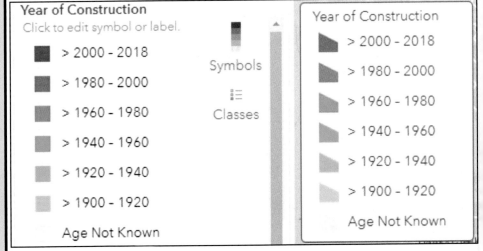

Year of Construction
Click to edit symbol or label.
■ > 2000 - 2018
■ > 1980 - 2000
■ > 1960 - 1980
■ > 1940 - 1960
■ > 1920 - 1940
■ > 1900 - 1920
Age Not Known

Symbols

Classes

Year of Construction
> 2000 - 2018
> 1980 - 2000
> 1960 - 1980
> 1940 - 1960
> 1920 - 1940
> 1900 - 1920
Age Not Known

16 **If you are not continuing, exit AGOL.**

Well that was a lot more complex than it seemed at the start, but you got through it very well!

Permissions and Security Settings

The last thing to look at in this chapter is setting the permissions and other security settings on the layers you just worked with. The three main selections for sharing are the owner, everyone in your organization, or everyone in the world (public). As you saw in chapter 4 Groups can also be used to control who has access or editing capabilities to certain data sets. For instance you may make a group for a select group of members in your organization, then share a restricted layer with only yourself (Owner) plus the group you made. If a layer is set to allow editing, then everyone you share with can edit – even if you set the sharing to public. This might be for a crowd-source project or something similar, but always be careful when you make a public dataset editable and remember that the authoritative level of the data may go down. In the emergency response world, it is rare that a response dataset is made editable and public. But if the data does need to be viewable by a larger audience, just not editable, you can always create a view of the data and set different sharing parameters on it.

Exercise 5e – Setting Sharing Parameters

Earlier you created and configured a host of different feature layers. It might seem easy to just make everything shared as a public file, but depending on the data the files contain this may not be the best thing to do. As a quick example, you will look at a scenario where some of the filed you created are going to be used in a job scheduling app for an area of Ft. Worth. Some aspects of the app will be viewable by the public so that they can track the progress of recovery jobs happening in their neighborhood and some will only be visible (and editable) by the crew members working on the jobs.

For this exercise you will set the edit and sharing capabilities for the layers FtWorthParcels, Public Works Team Assignments, and Active Public Works Jobs.

1 Open and log in to ArcGIS Online (if necessary). Go to the Content tab and open the GIS Guidebooks _Disaster folder.

First you will check the settings for the FtWorthParcels layer. This is public information, but is static and does not need to be editable. By now you are getting a long list of items in this folder, so the best way to find the target layers is to search for them.

2 At the top of the screen look for the search bar.

> Q Search GIS Guidebooks - Disaster

Note that the search tool is already configured to search just the active folder. If you need to search all your files you can select the All My Content folder … or if you need to search for files that anyone working the disaster may have created you can move to the My Groups or My Organization tabs and search through the file list from mother user's accounts, too.

3 Type in *FtWorth* and click return and you will see the feature layers matching this search.

Rafael's Question – What if I don't remember what I called a layer or I spell out Fort Worth instead of using the abbreviation? How do I find that data?

Here's the benefit of adding good documentation – and getting that Item Information slider to HIGH. The Search tool will look for key words in all the documentation for a layer including the description, summary, tags, categories, credits, and more so adding all that to a layer pays off when you use do a search. If you searched for Tornado you would still get the FtWorthParcels layer in the returned list because the description has that word in it. Populate Your Metadata! I'm often asked the question "Do you really have time to fill all this in during a disaster?" and I say YES because it has the potential to save you so much more time in the future.

4 Find the FtWorthParcels layer and look at the icons associated with it. This will indicate its sharing level.

It is currently shared with the Organization and the Recovery Team group. You want to share this publicly and add group sharing for your Disaster Exercises group. This can be done one of two ways. You can check the box next to a layer in the Content list, then click Share on the toolbar. This has the advantage of changing the sharing for multiple layers at one since all the feature layers checked will be changed. The other way is to open the Item Details and clicking the Share button on the tool list. Either method will open the same Share dialog.

5 Open the Item Details for the FtWorthParcels feature layer. Click the Share tab.

6 Select Everyone (public), then click the Edit Group Sharing button. From the list, select your Disaster Exercises group you made in chapter 1. Click OK, then Save.

7 Next move to the Settings tab and scroll down to see if editing is enabled. If it is uncheck the box and click Save, otherwise leave it alone and return to the Content tab.

Next you'll check the Public Works Team Assignments layer. This should be editable, and because of that it shouldn't be public. Unless you are doing a crowd-sourced project it's not a good idea to have an editable layer shared to the public. It would be too easy for someone to corrupt your data and ruin the work of a lot of people. Two ways to control this would be to share it with your organization – meaning that it would be password protected but anyone in the organization can edit it. The other way would be to leave it shared only to the owner and add a group sharing – meaning that anyone you add to a specific group could edit the layer but others, even if they are in your organization, could not. For this example, use the group sharing to restrict access.

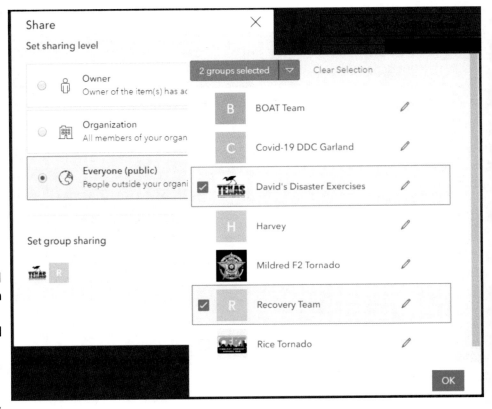

8 Open the Item Details for the Public Works Team Assignments layer and click Share (or check it in the Contents list and click Share).

9 Leave the sharing level to only the Owner, then click the Edit Group Sharing box. Check the box next to your Disaster Exercises group and any other groups that that you would like, then click OK and Save.

10 Next move to the Settings tab and verify that editing is enabled (and change if necessary).

So this layer will be editable, but only by users that you include in your group. And recall earlier that you made a 'view' of this data called Active Public Works Jobs. The intent of a view layer is to have something that can be made public but has different access rules than the source layer. Remember also that the view layer is displaying the same data from the source layer, so when the source is updated the view layer will reflect that. If shared publicly, confirm that it is not editable.

11 From the Content tab, open the Items Details for the Active Public Works Jobs layer.

12 Confirm that the layer is shared to Everyone (public), add the Group Sharing for your Disaster Exercises group, and verify that editing is not enabled.

Rafael's Question – Why did you set the two public layers to also be controlled by the group? Can't EVERYONE see these?

Yes, but by adding them to the Group they will also appear in the listing of the group's contents. To verify this click the My Groups tab, then click the Disaster Exercises group name in the list of groups. And if you used the option of creating a web page for the group, this is how you get them to appear on that page, too.

13 **Log out and close AGOL.**

That wraps up the sharing settings for this group of feature layers, and it demonstrates how to use the share and group options to secure your data.

Chapter 6 – Making Web Maps

In the first chapters of this book you have worked with all kinds of data, and set up untold parameters for pick lists, field names, visualization, sharing, and much more. All of that is leading up to making the data visible in a map. Maps must be created to house your feature layers, which can later be used in web apps (later in this book). The more time you spent configuring your feature layers, the better the layers will look in your map. And the more time you spend configuring your map, the better they will look in your web apps (which you'll build later in this book).

Making Web Maps with ArcGIS Pro

One of the best and easiest ways to build a web map is through ArcGIS Pro. All of the configurations you make in the Pro project for field aliases, pop-ups, symbolization, labeling, etc... will be transferred to your AGOL feature layer. Even if you use symbols that aren't typically in the AGOL styles, they will be transferred up and used. Because of this it is a great way to start a web map.

You saw the controls in AGP before for sharing a web layer (feature layer), and right beside that button is one for sharing a Web map. This process will share ALL the layers in the project to a feature layer, then build a web map for that feature layer. Note that you cannot do this individually from a layer's context menu, the whole project has to be shared. And remember that the data is copied to your AGOL account so future edits on this data done in AGP will not be reflected in your AGOL instance. But an interesting thing … you can change configurations in AGP then overwrite the AGOL web map, which will also replace the data and carry with it any edits you have made.

There are some important things to note when making web maps this way. First, if you have added any hosted data that is not stored locally, for example layers from your Portal or Enterprise instance as well as layers from other portals or the Living Atlas of the World, these layers will be transferred to the new web map. Another concern is having an active Join or Relate in the project. Joined or related tables are not supported in AGOL so the share process will fail. And finally is the use of an Esri basemap in your project. The basemap itself cannot be shared, but this will not stop the share process. All the valid layers except the basemap will be shared, then the new web map will be created using the same basemap you had in the ArcGIS Pro project.

Exercise 6a – Sharing a AGP Project as a Web Map

In this scenario you will use a AGP project that was made to show Covid-19 case counts by county across the state (of Texas, of course). During the pandemic the data was released by a state agency every day with new numbers, and this example data has values through May 2nd, 2020. The map in this project has carefully set symbology and pop-ups for the county data, and scale dependencies for the features and labels in the city data layer. Much of this was done with Arcade expressions, a language which will transfer seamlessly to AGOL and have the same functionality. Be careful if you use other languages in making pop-up expressions because they won't automatically transfer and you would need to rewrite them in AGOL after you publish the web map.

When this project is shared as a web map, it will have the same functionality as the project except that it will be available for others to see and use. But also understand that because AGOL and AGP are different technologies, there will always be some aspects of the AGP map that won't transfer well to AGOL. It's always best to keep things simple and concise, making sure that you are not loading too large of a dataset or too complex an Arcade script into AGOL. These things could create too much of a processing overhead and slow the response time. For example if I had a large dataset with a definition query that cut out half of the data, the AGOL web map would also have to store that large amount of data adding a storage burden for data that isn't used. Or if I had a super complex Arcade expression calculating a special field, because the expression calculates on the fly each time the map is zoomed or panned it might slow the display time. In this example you might want to make a special, smaller dataset to share or create field and calculate the value into it rather than rely on the expression.

1 **Start ArcGIS Pro and open the project Exercise 6a.**

2 **Zoom up to an area and notice the scale dependent features for cities.**

3 Click a county to see the pop-up. Note that if you click the line in the chart, nothing happens.

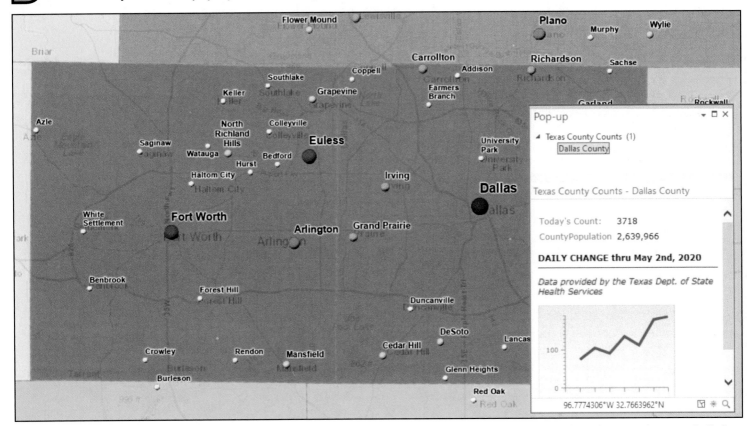

Very simple and straightforward – only one layer has a pop-up configured so that you control what the user sees, and all the information you want to present is in the pop-up (even though there's a lot more data in the actual dataset). If you like, you can explore the pop-up configuration a bit more to see how the chart was configured with Arcade. All these characteristics make a good web map, even if this might be a very good working or editing map.

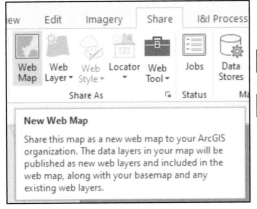

4 Zoom the map back to the full state view (bookmark FullView).

5 In the main toolbar click the Share tab, then click Web Map.

6 Provide a title of *Daily_Covid19_Change_Rate_Web_Map* along with appropriate summary and tags. Set the Folder to GIS Guidebooks – Disaster. Set the sharing to Everyone, and include the group Disaster Exercises. BUT DON'T CLICK SHARE YET.

There is another thing to set, and that is the Select a Configuration line. There are three choices and your selection will control how the web map can be used in AGOL. Note that if you sharing to an Enterprise portal the options include sharing a reference to registered data rather than copying the data, but for AGOL the data will always be copied.

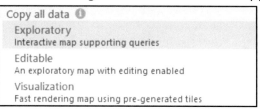

Exploratory – all the data will be copied to your AGOL account and set up non-editable feature layers. The sharing will mimic the share settings for the new web map.

Editable - all the data will be copied to your AGOL account and set up editable feature layers. The sharing will mimic the share settings for the new web map so be careful of sharing as public.

Visualization - all the data will be copied to your AGOL account and set up as tiled feature layers. The sharing will mimic the share settings for the new web map. Note that although the layers will draw quickly they cannot be queried. This is very suitable for making your own base maps but nor for making interactive data layers to be used in other items such as Dashboards.

7 Set the Configuration to Exploratory. Click Analyze and if there are no major errors, click Share.

8 When the process completes, the tool dialog box will display a link to the new web map. Click to open it.

9 You will be taken to the Item Details page for the new web map. Click Open in Map Viewer using the Beta version.

10 Zoom up to an area and click a county to see the pop-up. Click on the line in the chart and see what happens – this functionality isn't available in AGP.

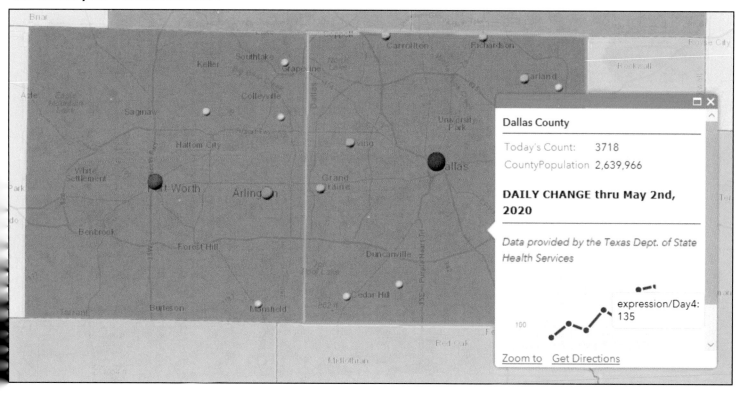

All the Arcade expressions transferred seamlessly along with all the map functionality. The layers were set with the visualization already configured, too, so if you add the feature layers to another map they will be symbolized the same and have the same labels and pop-ups. If you like, try looking at some of the configurations to see how they are set up. With that, the web map is ready to use. Note - IF you opened this in the original map viewer the labels may not have worked.

Building a Web Map in ArcGIS Online

The other way to build a web map is to use the Map Viewer in ArcGIS Online. The process is to start a new map and add the layers into it that you wish to participate in the display. If a layer has been configured and saved in the Visualization tab the layer will come in ready to use. If not it will come in with the default settings and you will need to configure it. It is also possible to take a configured layer and reset all of the configurations without altering the source settings. These configurations include:

- Change Style (symbology)
- Filter (definition query)
- Transparency
- Set Visibility Range (visible scale)
- Manage Labels
- Configure Pop-up

AGOL contains the original Map View and the Beta Map Viewer. For the most part both will have the same functionality just presented in a different format. But there are some buggy differences in the Beta version that certainly will get resolved. Because of this, these exercises will use the original Map Viewer but will demonstrate some of the Beta viewer's differences.

Exercise 6b – Build a New Wen Map

In this scenario you will use some of the layers you have created and configured in previous exercises to make a web map. This will be for the area in Ft Worth where you already have building footprints, and parcels, then you will add the layers for the Public Works team assignments. This map will be used in an editable web app so that the supervisor can assign public works teams to a job location. That will involve editing one layer and using the other layers as reference.

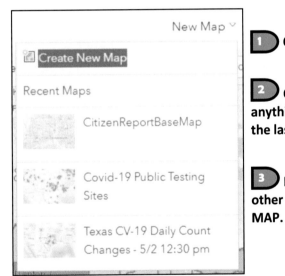

1 Open and log in to your AGOL account if necessary.

2 Click the Map tab – if any warning pop up just ignore them without saving anything. There may be some layers in the map already since this will default to the last map you opened.

3 In the upper right, click New Map > Create New Map. If presented with another pop-up, click YES, OPEN THE MAP.

The map will open with a default base map, and the Details column will give a four step guide on making a map. You are ready to start adding and configuring layers.

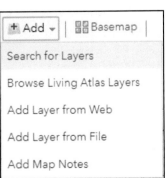

4 In the upper left click Add > Search for Layers

<————

5 In the Search dialog, type Ft Worth. Three layers will be shown.

————>

6 One-by-one, click the plus sign next to the FtWorthParcels and Ft_Worth_Tornado_Buildings layers.

7 Next search for Public Works. Add the layer Public Works Team Assignments.

8 Then click the Back arrow to return to the layers list. Depending on what you have done with the Map Viewer before you may have to click the Content tab to see the layers list.

9 Note also that the map may have zoomed to another location – the default extents of the Public Works layer. Click the options button next to the Ft Worth Tornado Buildings layer and select Zoom To.

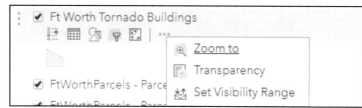

10 In the upper toolbar click Save > Save and name the map FtWorth_PW_Maintenance_Map. Provide tags and summary, set the destination folder, then click Save Map.

The layers are added but are not configured for the desired use.

Start with configuring the building footprints as a dark grey polygon with these settings:

- Change Style – gray polygon with a black border
- Filter - none
- Transparency - none
- Set Visibility Range -visible at all scales
- Manage Labels - none
- Configure Pop-up – disable pop-up

The controls for configuring layers are shown here. Refer to this as you continue. Note that if these are not visible for a layer, click on the layer name.

11 Click the Options button and select Rename and shorten the name to just Buildings.

12 Click the Change Style button. The available styles are shown and the circle with the check mark in it identifies which style is being used. Click Options.

13 Click the word Symbols and the selection dialog opens. Note that this can set both the fill and the outline. Select a dark gray. Note that you can set a transparency for the fill that is independent of the outline.

14 Click the Outline button. Set the color to black. Note that this also allows an independent transparency settings, as well as controls for line width and pattern.

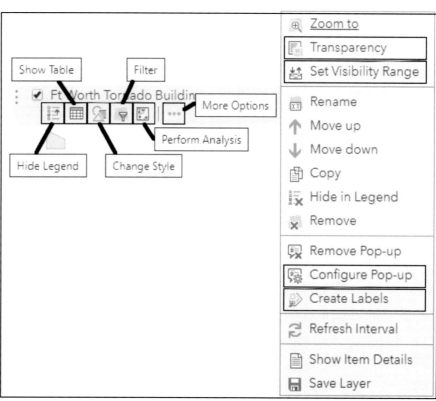

53

15 After setting the colors, click OK, OK, and Done.

16 Lastly, click the Options button and select Remove Pop-up.

Next configure the FtWorthParcels layer. It will have these settings:

- Change Style – tan polygon with a black border
- Filter - none
- Transparency – 75%
- Set Visibility Range -visible at all scales
- Manage Labels – Label with address number (optional)
- Configure Pop-up – Display the GIS Link as the title, the Property Class, Situs_Address, all the owner information, and the year of construction.

17 Click the Options button and rename the layer Property Information.

18 Click the Change Style button and set to "Show Location Only".

19 Click Options and set the Symbol fill and outline as described above. Then set the transparency to 75%.

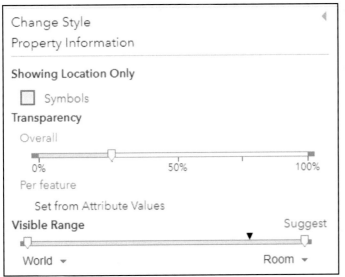

This next step on setting the label is optional depending on how much Arcade you want to learn. The instructions here are minimal so if you are totally clueless on Arcade you may want to skip this step.

Ideally the data would have a field containing the address number, but in this case it does not. There is, however, a field called Situs_Address and that has the address number at the start of it. The trick will be to clip off the number and display only that.

There is a common programmer's solution – look for the first space and clip off all the characters that appear before it. In most instances this will be the address number, but you may see a few that don't fit this form and that'll be OK.

The function to locate the space has this syntax -

find(SearchString, field_name) so you'll type find(" ",$feature[SitusAddress]).

This is where the space is located, so subtracting 1 from this will be how many character to get from the front of the field value.

Then you can use this function to extract the address numbers -

Left(field_name, CharCount)).

Even better, by embedding the find() function in the Left() function you can do this in one step, which is highly desirable in Arcade expressions:

Left($feature["Situs_Address"],(find(" ",$feature["Situs_Address"]))-1)

20 From the options menu select Create Labels. Click the Text drop down, then scroll to the bottom and select Custom (Expression).

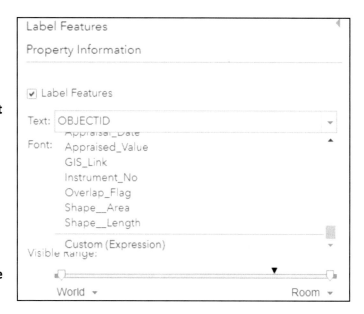

21 If you know how to use the Arcade expression builder, use that – otherwise type in the expression above. Click Test and if successful click OK.

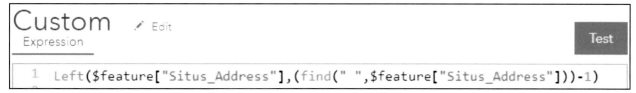

22 Check the box to make the labels visible (if necessary), click the box to add a 1 pt halo, and set the upper limit of the Visible Range to Buildings. Click OK.

23 The last thing to set is the pop-up. Click the options button and select Configure Pop-up.

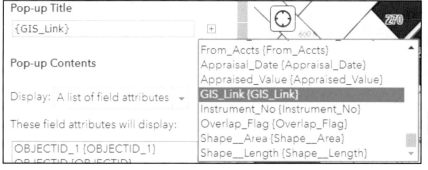

24 Delete the default Title, click the plus sign next to the entry box, and scroll down to GIS_Link. Click to add it to the entry box.

25 Next click Configure Attributes in configuration menu.

The Configure Attributes box will display all the fields in this layer – which are a LOT. A quick way to turn them all on or off is using the check box next to Display. Clicking once turns them all on and clicking a second time turns them all off.

As you work through this configuration, take the time to check every entry for a proper Field Alias and proper number formatting. This includes the number of decimal places and the use of a thousands separator. For example, you wouldn't want to display the 'Year of Construction' as 2,013.00.

26 Click the Display checkbox on, then off to turn all the fields off. The selectively turn on the fields mentioned above – taking the time to build an attractive field alias for them. Click OK and OK again when done.

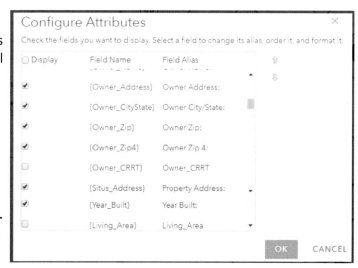

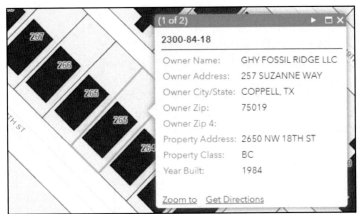

Owner Name: GHY FOSSIL RIDGE LLC
Owner Address: 257 SUZANNE WAY
Owner City/State: COPPELL, TX
Owner Zip: 75019
Owner Zip 4:
Property Address: 2650 NW 18TH ST
Property Class: BC
Year Built: 1984

Zoom to   Get Directions

27 **Click on a parcel to test the pop-up and correct any issues you see.**

Rafael's Question – I don't like the way the Zip Code looks. Is it possible to have this on a single line?

Yes – you can build an Arcade expression to concatenate these onto a single line, then instead of displaying the two fields you would display the Arcade expression. If you want to try this, in the configuration menu click Attribute Expressions. Then build the expression:

```
1   $feature["Owner_Zip"] + "-" + $feature["Owner_Zip4"]
```

Then go back to the Configure Attributes interface and move the new expression up to the other Zip Code fields. Thurn them off and turn the expression on instead – making sure it has an appropriate alias.

Owner Name: ARGUELLO, RAUL
Owner Address: 2616 NW 19TH ST
Owner City/State: FORT WORTH, TX
Zip Code   76106-5017

The layer FtWorthParcels – Parcel Boundaries is already configured correctly so you leave it untouched.

The last layer to configure is the Public Works Team Assignments layer. It should have these settings:

- Change Style – Symbolize with unique values using the Job Description field.
- Clearing Road – red w/ black outline
- Controlling Traffic – light blue w/ black outline
- Inspecting Damage – orange w/ black outline
- Setting Up Barricades – dark blue w/ black outline
- Filter - none
- Transparency – 75%
- Set Visibility Range -visible at all scales
- Manage Labels – Label with Team Name
- Configure Pop-up – Display the Team Name as the title, the Dispatch Time, the Elapsed Time, and the Job Description.

First you can set the style. Because you set up a picklist for the Job Description field in an earlier exercise, the style is already set to Types (Unique Symbols) so you can just set the colors. You can also set the outline, but make sure that none of the individual components of the symbols has a transparency – it's better to control this with the overall layer setting except in special circumstances.

28 **Click the Change Styles button under the Public Works Team Assignments layer. Then click Options.**

29 **Click each of the colors and set them according to the list above. Click OK and Done.**

You should go through the list of layers and confirm all the settings. It's also a good time to decide if any of the layers can be hidden in the legend and tweak the transparency or visibility range.

There is also an option to control Refresh Interval. This determines how often a layer is refreshed from the stored layer. For layers like the building footprints, parcels, or parcel lines (those that are not changing) the refresh rate can be set to zero , meaning that the layer will refresh when the user zooms or pans. Otherwise the data remains statics. For other layers like the Public Works Team Assignments the refresh rate should be higher. When new polygons are drawn you will want the layer to refresh so that all the apps consuming this layer will see the new information as soon as possible. For a long-term project like damage assessment you could set the refresh rate at ten or more minutes, but for the team assignments you will want to set it to about 1 minute.

30 **Open the Options for the Public Works Team Assignments layer and click Refresh Interval. Set it to 1 min.**

The only thing left is to test out the map settings and tweak if necessary.

31 **Zoom in to an area and note if the parcels labels go on and off as expected. Then click a parcel and examine the pop-up. Finally click Edit in the top menu and try drawing in polygons representing various team assignments, giving them team names and realistic dispatch times. Make sure that they are colored and labeled correctly.**

32 **If everything checks out OK, save the map and return to the Content page.**

These are the very basic things to set up, but you can also set up other information in the Configure Pop-up dialog. In this map you'll look at a basic expression and in the next some more complex things.

The Public Works Team Assignments layer included a field for Dispatch Time (and when you drew some sample polygons you gave them a realistic date and time, and if no go back and do that). It would be nice if you had an indicator of how long they've been on the job display in the pop-up. There is a field for Elapsed Time but that's to be calculated after the jobs are done, not displayed on-the-fly. To do this you can write an Arcade expression to calculate the time difference between that field and the current time. The function for the calculation is called DateDiff and the function for time is called Now(). This is an optional part so if you aren't familiar with Arcade you can skip ahead.

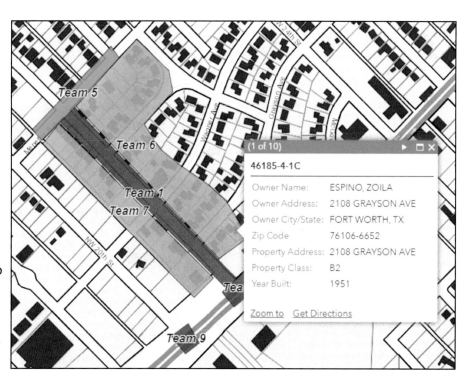

Rafael's Question – what's the big deal about Arcade? Isn't it just another programming language I have to learn?

Arcade's 'big deal' is that it works seamlessly across all the ArcGIS platforms without having to modify code in any way. Expressions you build in AGP will work in AGOL without modification. And it's not a programming language in that you can't write stand-alone programs with it. It has to run inside an ArcGIS software. And it's pretty simple to learn (I know a good book!).

1 Open the **FtWorthPW_Management Map** in the map viewer (if you closed it).

2 Click the **Public Works Team Assignments** layer and select **Configure Pop-ups**.

3 Find the **Attribute Expressions** area near the bottom of the page and click **Add**.

4 The **Expression Builder** dialog opens. At the top, click the **Edit** button and rename the expression "**Time On Job**".

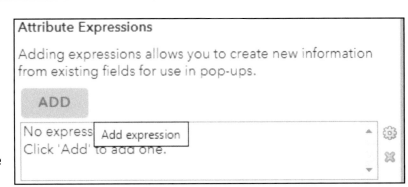

5 If you are familiar with Arcade you can use the builder tools to make the expression, otherwise type as shown.

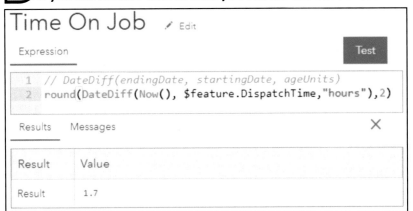

6 Go back and open the **Configure Attributes** dialog. You will see that the new expression has been added to the fields list, and the title of the expression is used as the field alias.

7 Turn off the **Elapsed Time** field and move the **Time On Job** field up in the list. Then click OK, and OK.

8 Click on one of the team assignment polygons and note the pop-up. In this example a lot of items were selected and the second pop-up was for the team assignment.

Hey Rafael – there's the other "big deal" about Arcade. It created an expression that will calculate a value on-the-fly every time the pop-up box is opened. Wait ten minutes and click on that item again!

9 Save and close the map and return to the Content tab.

You see how pop-ups can provide information about an item in a layer using both the attributes from the table as well as calculated values.

Adding Charts to the Pop-ups

In this next exercise you'll see how to add charts and other graphics to a pop-up. These can include:

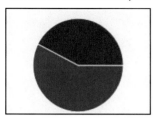

Pie charts – each value you select will be a wedge in the pie. All the values together should represent the "whole" of something. For example if you did a pie chart of all age groups, together they would represent the total population. Or a breakdown of taxes (school vs. property vs. special districts) would represent all taxes paid on a piece of property. But you wouldn't want to show things that were not in the same category, such as Count of Pine Trees vs. Number of Cars. These when totaled don't represent the "whole" of something.

Bar charts – Each value is represented by a horizontal bar in the chart. This offers the viewer a visual comparison between values.

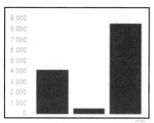

Columns charts – each value is represented by a vertical column in the chart. Exactly the same as the bar chart except in a vertical format.

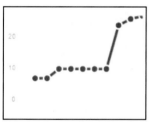

Line charts – each value is shown as a dot on the chart and connected with a line. These work best when a series of fields represent the values over time such as daily rain measurements or daily traffic counts. Note that only one line can be drawn.

Images – this will display any thumbnail image called with a URL and can have an optional link attached to it. This would be best used to display a company logo or a pre-made chart from another package, then linking a site with more information about the data (or its source) being used. It would not, however, lend itself to displaying a complex image or chart due to the limited display size.

Choosing the right type of chart can be a little intimidating but they are easy to make (and delete) so maybe its best to try a few and delete the ones that don't look good.

Exercise 6c – Making a Chart

In this exercise you will make a new map and add the 2016 Daytime Population data that you referenced in a previous exercise from the Living Atlas. One thing to note here is that you can show the data and make expressions even though the data is read-only. You will start by making a new map and adding this data to it.

1 **Open ArcGIS Online and login (if necessary).**

2 On the main menu click on Map. Then in the upper right click the pulldown under New Map and select Create new Map. Note the list of previous maps.

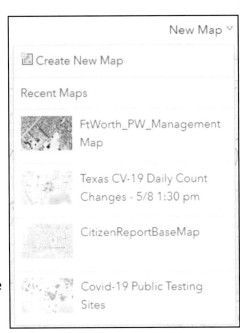

New Map ⌄

📄 Create New Map

Recent Maps

FtWorth_PW_Management Map

Texas CV-19 Daily Count Changes - 5/8 1:30 pm

CitizenReportBaseMap

Covid-19 Public Testing Sites

3 Click Add > Search for Layers, then search for Daytime Population.

4 Click the Plus sign to add the data, then return to the map.

You will see that the contents of the map now lists three layers, all viewable at different scales. For the exercise you will only work with one of the layers, and you can always go back and configure the others alter as additional practice.

5 Zoom in to any are you choose until the USA Daytime Population 2016 – Tracts becomes visible.

6 Click on any of the diamond symbols to open the pop-up.

This pop-up displays all of the fields from the data layer. You're goal is to display the Daytime Population: Workers and Daytime Population: Residents as a chart. When you add them as a chart you will also want to remove them from the fields list so that the same data isn't displayed twice.

7 Click the Options button under Daytime Population Tracts and select Configure Pop-up.

8 Click the Configure Attributes button and uncheck the two fields that you'll use in the chart, then click OK.

9 Scroll down to the area titled Pop-up Media and click on Add, then select Pie Chart.

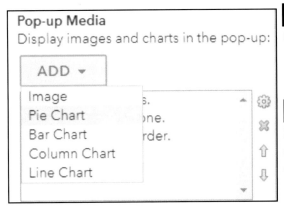

Pop-up Media
Display images and charts in the pop-up:

ADD ▾

Image
Pie Chart   ne.
Bar Chart   rder.
Column Chart
Line Chart

10 Change the title to *Workers vs. Residents* with a caption *Count of Daytime Workers and Residents Population – 2016*

11 Scroll down in the Chart Fields list and check the two fields Daytime Population: Workers and Daytime Population: Residents. Click the alias of each field and shorten them to *Workers -* and *Residents -* . Click OK. Then click OK to close the configuration pane.

Chart Fields

	Field Alias	Field Name
☐	Field Alias	Field Name
☑	Workers	{DPOPWRK_CY}
☑	Residents	{DPOPRES_CY}
☐	Shape__Area	{Shape__Area}
☐	Shape__Length	{Shape__Length}

12 Click on any symbol in the map, scroll to the bottom of the pop-up and note the results.

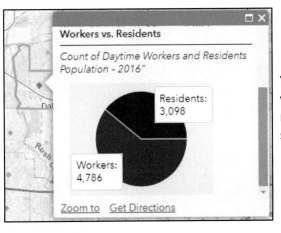

Workers vs. Residents

Count of Daytime Workers and Residents Population - 2016"

Residents: 3,098

Workers: 4,786

Zoom to Get Directions

You can see your title, caption, and if you hover over each slice of the pie you will see your new Alias tag and value. Note that the simplified aliases make for a cleaner presentation in the chart than if you had kept the preset, longer alias.

Rafael's Question – that pie chart is very nice, but would one of the other chart types work better?

The type of data and the audience of the map can help you determine the best chart – but so can making one of each and looking at them. Since this does represent the "whole" of something the use of the pie chart is certainly valid, but if you like you can make one of each of the other types and see if another type might be more appropriate.

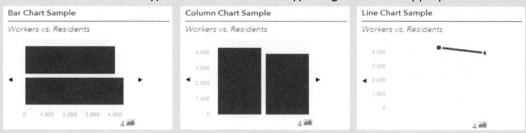

The Bar and Column charts would certainly be OK, but I think the pie shows the data the best. The line chart in this instance is confusing. Go back to the configuration pane and remove the charts you no longer want to use.

Note the arrows at the sides of the charts to aid in navigation, and the icon at the lower right showing the user how many charts are in the collection. This is called the Carousel.

13 **Using the chart style you decided upon, repeat the chart configuration for the 'Counties' and 'State' layers.**

14 **Save the map as *Daytime Population – Workers vs. Residents*.**

Note that there is not an automatic save when making maps in AGOL. You can easily exit the Map interface without saving and possible lose work, so make saving (or in some instances NOT saving) a deliberate act.

Custom Expressions—Arcade

You can see that configuring the charts isn't very difficult, but it may be hard deciding upon the style to use. In this instance the Line style wasn't the best, but for data collected over time it will be much more appropriate.

Besides making a chart, you may also want to make a custom expression to show an aspect of the data that isn't reflected in the stock fields. The expressions are written in Arcade, and you've seen a bit of that already. This time you'll make a custom expression and use it in a chart.

Exercise 6d – Using Custom Expressions in Charts

In this exercise you will use some of the actual Covid-19 count data for the State of Texas. The data contains the daily count for each county in Texas for 8 days. Each count represents the cumulative count up to that point in time, but the map needs to show the "rate of change" or the difference in each day's count. The term "flattening the curve" that was heard often during the start of the pandemic means that you are looking for the point when the new cases per day starts to level off or decrease. The data, however, only contains the daily count so you will have to calculate the change values on the fly with an Arcade expression.

The data is in a zipped shapefile in the Exercise 6d folder of the book's dataset. You should know how to make that into a feature layer.

1 **Start ArcGIS Online, if necessary, and make a new feature layer called Daily_Covid_By_County_TX using the shape-file CovidCountyCounts_TX.zip. Store it in the GIS Guidebooks – Disaster folder.**

2 **In the Item Details page for the new layer, click the Data tab and examine both the existing data table and the field list.**

The data is fully populated, and the field list will reveal a series of values labeled Day 1 to Day 8, with Day 1 being 'today' and the others counting back in time to 8 days ago. Note also the Population field. The data will be symbolized by the daily change from Day 2 to Day 1, normalized by population.

Although the visualization can be done in the Item Details screen, in this case you will practice configuring the map directly in the Map Viewer.

3 **From the Detail Overview page, open the feature layer in the Map Viewer.**

Note – as of this writing the Beta map viewer doesn't support charts so while it would be fun to do some experimenting, this is not the time. It's also not a good time during an active disaster to experiment with Beta version so knowing the functionality and/or limitations of the basic versions is key.

You will start by completing some tasks that you've done n other exercises (so no pictures provided).

4 Change the layer's title to *Daily Covid-19 Count by County*.

5 Set the Transparency to 25%.

6 Click the Style button, then next to Choose an Attribute to Show click the Edit Expression tool.

7 In the Expression Builder dialog change the expression title to Count Per 1K Population. Then build the expression shown. Click OK.

8 Change the OPTIONS button under Counts and Amounts (color).

9 Set the color to a light to dark orange. Next click Classify Data, leave the method as Natural Breaks, and change the number of classes to 5. Then click OK and Done.

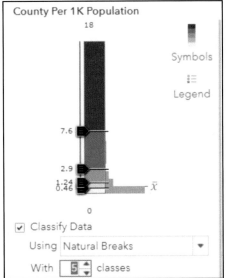

10 Now's a good time to save the map, proving an appropriate title and summary.

By using an expression here, you are symbolizing by a value that didn't previously exist in the dataset. Note that when you build Arcade expressions (and you'll learn this in the Arcade book) you want to make them as condensed as possible to limit the over processing required when the map redraws. In this case it is calculating the value each time you zoom or pan for each of the 254 counties. Not a tremendous amount of processing overhead but imagine doing this for thousands of features.

Next you will configure the pop-up to show only certain fields, as well as a chart using expression values.

11 Click Options, then Configure Pop-ups.

12 Change the title to *Daily Change in Count*.

Before any of the configurations can be done, like configuring fields and charts, you should go ahead and build the expressions that will be used. The first one will be easy since it will be a formatted version of the current day's count. This value is already in a field (Day1) but by doing this in an expression you can control how it is displayed as well as change the field alias.

13 In the Attribute Expressions area click Add. The expression builder pane opens.

14 Change the title to *Today's Count* and build the expression shown. Click OK.

15 Next click Configure Attributes.

The map viewer by default will have several of the attributes displayed, but in this instance there are some that will be used in the charts that you don't want displayed. So you will selectively set this.

There's a control at the top that let's you select all the fields, and when they are all selected it changes to let you de-select all the fields.

16 Uncheck all of the fields (Hint: check the Display box twice), then check the fields Name, Population, and the new expression Today's Count. Click OK.

Rafael's Question – I tested this pop-up and the county name is just shown as a name without the word County. Wouldn't it make more sense if the value displayed as "Jones County" instead of just "Jones".

Yes, but that's not what's in the data set. All the reports we are using to compile this data just have the name without the word county so changing the data would really mess things up. HOWEVER – you could build a custom expression to concatenate the word " County" to the end of the name and have it look nicer. Remember that expressions can show the values in new and different ways. Go do that if you like!

Before you make the chart, there's an important lesson to know about using values in charts. The values will display in the chart using the order in which they appear in the fields list. The field highest up the list will appear as the left value of a column chart and the bottom value of a bar chart. If the fields are not appearing the correct order, you can go into the Configure Attributes list and reorder them. Note that the reordering of fields to control their order in a chart is supported in AGOL, but it is not supported in AGP. When you make expressions to use in a chart, the same rules apply. The expression highest in the list will appear at the left of a column chart and the bottom of a bar chart.

The next important thing to know is that the charts can only show numeric values, so if you are making custom expressions make sure they don't format as text. For example, previous exercises used the Arcade function text() to format a number to show commas and then concatenate them to other text strings. To use a value in a chart with formatting you have to use the Arcade function number().

For this chart, you want to show the change in values day by day, not the count of values. You can get the daily change by making seven expressions, each of which subtract one day's value from another. But be careful to make the expression in the correct order so that they will appear correctly in the columns chart – in other words make the change expression for seven days ago first, then work through all the expressions with the change in today's value being last.

17 In the Attribute Expressions area click Add. The expression builder pane opens.

18 Change the title to *Day 7 Change*. Then write the expression below. Click OK.

```
1   $feature.Day7 - $feature.Day8
```

19 Build six more expressions for the daily changes. Make sure to set the titles for each, and subtract the previous day's value from that day's value (Hint: 7 from 6, 6 from 5, 5 from 4, etc...).

20 Note that new expressions are automatically made visible in the attribute list, so click Configure Attributes and uncheck all the new expressions.

21 In the Pop-up Media area click Add > Column Chart.

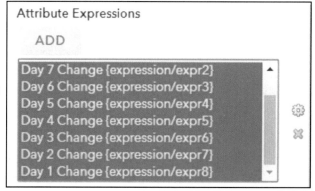

22 Set the title to *Daily Change in Count Values* and provide a summary. Then check the boxes for all the Day X Change expression. Note that it doesn't matter in which order you check them because they will display in the preset manner described above. Click OK, and OK again to exit the configuration pane.

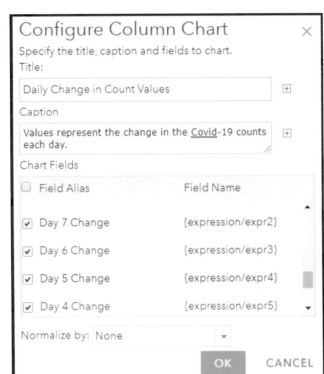

23 Click a county in the map to test the pop-up.

Rafael's Question – Why didn't we just make new fields in the table for the change in counts and calculate them? Why do that with an expression?

In this instance, we will get a new set of count data tomorrow. Instead of having to build and calculate a bunch more fields again (and every day from now on) these expression will just read the new data and make the calculations.

That map turned out pretty nice! You set the colors using an expression, then displayed a chart using more expressions. Even though the raw data coming from the state didn't have these exact values, you were still able to make the map you need.

Rafael's Challenge – having read the Arcade book, Rafael wants to add an expression to display in the attribute list showing the average change in counts over the past 7 days. This would give a frame of reference for the change values being shown in the charts. If you want to take this challenge on, go back into the Configure Pop-ups pane and set that up.

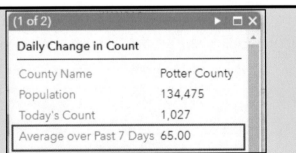

24 Save your map. If you are not continuing, exit AGOL.

All of the maps in this chapter look fantastic, but they are just Web Maps – not really suitable to put out for field use. Here are no real map controls, no analysis tools, no search tools, etc... For these to become a usable field map they need to be included in a Web App – and that's coming up later.

Chapter 7 – Data Collection Apps

With the other chapters in this book you've seen how to create data structures from scratch and how to import data from other sources. Many times in a disaster there's data out there that no one has captured yet, and we need a way for field crews to collect that data and send it back to us. In the olden days (a few years ago) we would send teams of people into the field with paper forms and a pencil and they would jot down their notes – then someone would have to take the paper forms and type the notes into this computer thing – then someone would have to correct all the misspelled words and decipher all the bad handwriting – then someone would have to try and put dots on the map corresponding to the locations described on the paper forms – then someone would run from the room screaming. The field crews might be out all day – then it was HOURS AND HOURS of work to get dots on a map that represented anything. Meanwhile everyone is waiting for the maps.

Then came the introduction of smart phone and tablet based collection programs that allow field crews to collect data digitally and have it appear on the map as each location is captured. Within minutes of the field crews finishing their collection, the maps are ready. EOC teams can even make decisions about the damage before the collections are finished. There is one big difference, though. It shifts the mapping work to the start of the disaster rather than the end. At first dawn the field crews will need to have apps ready to go so that they can get started.

Making Collection Apps

The main apps used by Texas EGRT are GeoForm, Collector, Survey 123, and Quick Capture. Each has its own strengths and weaknesses, and one may be more suitable than another in any given circumstance. This means that the mapping teams need to be very familiar with the capabilities of each app, when each is best deployed, and how to quickly set up an instance of the app BEFORE the disaster strikes. You do not want to be spending time learning an app while the field crews are waiting, nor do you want to send teams out with an app only to discover major faults – or worse, that you used the wrong app.

Note – Texas EGRT is not a field team, we are an office unit. We DO NOT go into the field and perform data collection. Our GIS Team is much more valuable in the EOC, so we rely on other volunteer groups to go into the field and perform the data collection.

One of the basic distinctions between all the apps is whether they are form based or map based – in other words does the user enter by interacting with a form or a map. Of the three, the only "mapcentric" app is Collector. The user sees a map that follows their current location. Then they click a button to add a new location and a pop-up windows opens and allows for data entry. When the entry is completed, the app returns to the map and shows symbolized features where all the data collection has happened. What's nice about this is that the user sees everyone else's work on their display and it may prevent the same location being collected twice.

The more "formcentric" apps are GeoForm, QuickCapture , and Survey 123. These present a configurable form to the user that prompts them to enter information. So which do you use and when? The GeoForm is a pretty simplistic form that you really don't want to put too many questions in, and it is limited to collecting point locations only. It can display a map in the form that is used to identify a location but it doesn't display other user collected points. The main use for this is crowdsource apps and forms intended for the simplest of users – not something your hard-code GIS expert would enjoy.

The QuickCapture app (AKA The Big Button App) is very robust and can collect points, line, or polygons. Its strength is that it is super easy to use and presents button menus rather than a lot of fill-in-the-blank forms. The app will capture a location, allow you to take a photo, and populate fields from a pick list presented to the user. It doesn't, however, allow you to type into a field so you need to know what all possible choices you want to make available before designing the app. Users then see a question and they answer it by pressing one of the predefine buttons.

Finally is Survey 123. It also allows the capture of points, lines, and polygons and display a map as part of the data collection. But it's strongest feature is the ability to configure the form to collect data in a large number of ways: type in a value, pick from a list, use a slider bar, click radio buttons, and many more. This is done using the XLSForm formatting codes in Excel spreadsheets, and the variety of options is staggering. With these codes you can basically recreate any printed form's look and feel, but make it a dynamic (and geographically aware) form that captures data and photos directly into your map. Consequently, it can be the most difficult to configure.

The most important feature in Survey 123 (at least for use in a disaster) is the accountability it has for the data that is collected. The app will store every survey on the local device, then identify the user's connectivity status and let them know when the survey is uploaded to the server. Why is this important? Using a very early release of Survey 123, Texas EGRT had a circumstance where a field team did 315 damage assessment surveys (both digitally and on paper) but when everyone came in there were only 297 dots on the map. We lost 18 surveys somewhere – with no way of knowing which didn't get uploaded. The tornado we were working had taken out several cell phone towers, and crew members with that brand of phone were not getting a signal in some areas and therefore were not uploading surveys when they pressed the button. This was our first use of the app and fortunately we did both the paper form and the digital form. After matching the paper forms with the digital attribute table we were able to find the missing surveys and get them entered. At that point we stopped using the app until Esri added the accountability features. If the same thing happened today we could quickly look on each device and see what surveys didn't upload – a very important failsafe. No one wants to be the guy that has to go to the Incident Commander and ask for the field crews to go back out and do more data collection because our app screwed up. Be careful, there's always an old-timer with a yellow pad and a crayon to say "I tolds ya them fone thangs wouldn't work". We've also had a CERT team member show up with a Jelly Pro phone (please go look that up).

When you are deployed for a disaster, you will need to know enough about these apps to pick the right one, and get an instance spun up in a hurry. But you also need to know what the app needs to accomplish (and this can help you decide which app to use). Take the time to sit down with a member of the field crew, hopefully their head guy, and ask what they need to accomplish. Will hundreds of people need to type in a few simple lines of information?? – maybe a GeoForm will work. Will teams whose main focus isn't data collection need a way to report information back to the EOC while they are doing their

Exercise 7a – Making a Simple Form App

In this exercise you are going to make both a GeoForm and a Quick Capture form using a feature layer. Then by seeing both in action you can get an idea of in which circumstances each might best be used.

For this scenario, a flash flood occurred down one of the creeks in town and has since receded. A lot of debris was swept into the creek and now the Public Works team is going to walk the creek, pick up trash and easily removed debris, and mark any large debris that will need heavy equipment to remove. At the same time you want residents along the creek to report any debris that may be in their yard so that you can remove it while the equipment is in the area. After some discussion with the Public Works Director, she has also asked that as long as the crews are walking the creek could they also capture the creek type (natural earth or concrete lined channel) and make a note of any storm drain outfalls they see. That data will be useful later on.

A GeoForm will be perfect for the citizens to use – they don't really need to take pictures or anything, just type in a report of their name, address, phone number, e-mail address, and a description of the debris. The debris question could even have a picklist of Brush, Trash, Other along with a text field for them to provide a better description. That can be a point layer with 6 fields.

The QuickCapture app will work well for the public Works crews since they will be focused on debris removal and not data collection, and they can record the data you want with a push of one of the big buttons. For this app, you will need a line feature layer with a field for type and the choices Natural Earth or Concrete Lined Channel. Then a point feature layer for Storm Drain Outfall, and go ahead and give them the choices of Pipe (round) or Box (square). And lastly you will need a point feature layer to record the location of large debris and you can give them the choice of Brush, Trash, Appliance, and Car.

You can start by making the feature layers describe above in AGOL, then fix up the fields and pick lists. Remember that you should talk with the fields crews before designing the feature layers and get an idea of what they want to accomplish and what data they need to collect. You can always suggest additional fields that you know they will need as long as you don't make the apps too cumbersome or difficult to use or understand. In this instance you will be dealing with non-GIS folks and you have to convince them that any additional work to populate the app is necessary.

Rafael's Question: Can I try this on my own first?

Since you asked I'll be super nice and "let" you do this – because you were going to have to do it anyway. Below is an outline of the layers, fields, and pick lists. Read it over, then make a new folder called Data Collection and go create these layers.

CitizenReports (points)

        Name – text (don't allow null values)

        Address – text (don't allow null values)

        Phone Number – text

        E-mail address - text

        Debris Type – text – "Brush", "Trash", "Other"

        Description – text

CreekBottom (lines)

        Type – text – "Natural Earth", "Concrete Lined"

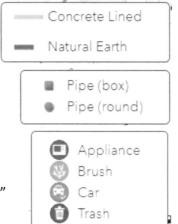

StormDrainOutfalls (points)

        PipeType – text – "Pipe (round)", "Box (square)"

LargeDebris (points)

        DebrisType – text – "Brush, "Trash", "Appliance", "Car"

Need some help getting started?

◊   On the Content tab, click the Create New Folder button. Name it Data Collection.

◊   Click the Create > Feature Layer button. Search for Points and click the Points template.

◊   During the create process, you don't need to check the "Capture GPS receiver information" box.

◊   Zoom to your area of interest (where you currently are so that you can test it).

◊   Fill out the Title, Tags, Summary, Category, and save it in the new folder.

◊   In the Layer Details screen, click the Data tab. Add the fields and/or value lists.

◊   Repeat for the other layers. If you can't finish, please review the earlier chapters on creating layers.

Next you can go into the Visualization tab for each layer and set the symbols. Using the fields with the pick lists, set the symbols for each layer. Some examples were provided above.

With these created and symbolized you can now make the web apps for the data collection. Start with the GeoForm.

In addition to the CitizenReports layer you will also need a web map to display the reports.

1 **Click the options button for the Citizen Reports layer and select Open in Map Viewer You can experiment with the BETA Map Viewer if you like, but remember that it doesn't support charts in pop-up yet.**

2 You may want to configure the pop-ups, set a label or select a symbology. When you are done, click Save and call the new map CitizenReportBaseMap.

3 Return to the Content tab.

A geoForm will show as a web application in your contents list. These are made using the layer you designed, the web map you created, and a wizard that will step you through the creation process.

4 In the Content tab, check the box next to the CitizenReports layer.

5 Then click Create and select Configurable Apps.

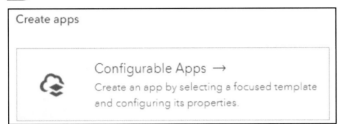

Create apps

Configurable Apps →
Create an app by selecting a focused template and configuring its properties.

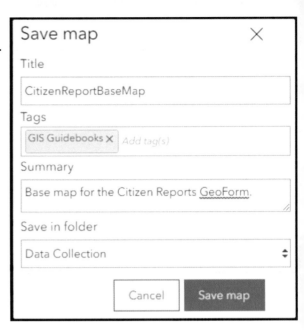

Save map   ✕

Title

CitizenReportBaseMap

Tags

GIS Guidebooks ✕   Add tag(s)

Summary

Base map for the Citizen Reports GeoForm.

Save in folder

Data Collection   ▲▼

                        Cancel   Save map

6 Click the Create/Edit Data category at the left, then select GeoForm and Create Web App.

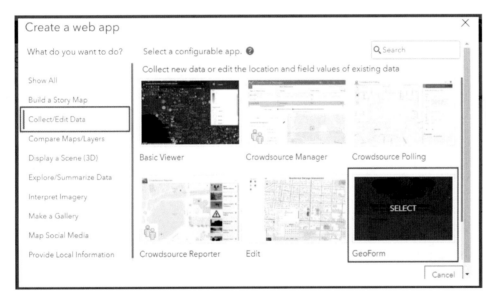

Create a web app   ✕

What do you want to do?   Select a configurable app. ❓   🔍 Search

Collect new data or edit the location and field values of existing data

Show All
Build a Story Map
Collect/Edit Data
Compare Maps/Layers   Basic Viewer   Crowdsource Manager   Crowdsource Polling
Display a Scene (3D)
Explore/Summarize Data
Interpret Imagery   SELECT
Make a Gallery
Map Social Media
Provide Local Information   Crowdsource Reporter   Edit   GeoForm

                                                          Cancel

You no doubt saw the Download option. This will let you download the source code for GeoFrom and use it to create GeoForms in your own portal.

7 Enter a Title, Tags, Summary, and Category and click Done. Use the scenario description above to determine what these should be.

Hint – make them VERY DESCRIPTIVE because these will be the title and prompts in your form.

At this point the wizard will walk you through the ten steps needed to create the form.

8 Read Step 1 and click Next.

9 Click Choose Webmap and select the CitizenReportBaseMap. Then click Next.

Select a Webmap

Select Web Map   ✕

My Content   ▼   CitizenReportBaseMap

CitizenReportB...

1 - 1 of 1 results

✏ Choose Webmap

← Previous   Preview   Nex   Ok   Cancel

Hint – you should type in the full name of the layer and search for it because the layers are listed in alphabetical order and the search doesn't do partial name searches. Otherwise you may have a hard time finding the layer.

10 Click Next on Step 3. Since you only have one layer in the map it by default will be selected.

You can see that if you had many other layers in the base map you could specify which layer is to be used in the form.

On Step 4 there are a lot of parameters you can set involving the title, instructions, and even the button labels. The Title and Instructions will default to the Title and Summary you provided with the layer, but this is your chance to override them. Notice also that you can include a logo. For this exercise you will disable it.

11) **Click Use Small Header and Disable Logo. Change the Submit Button Text to "Click to Submit Your Report". Then click Next.**

Step 5 lets you determine which fields should be displayed and allows for some optional display text. By clicking the Configure button next to any field you will be given options based on the field type. For these text fields you can add a hint or even suggest some entry text in the field.

This step also lets you decide whether or not to allow attachments. If you allow them, you can make them required, and even define the text for the button or add additional instructions on how to add an attachment. For this form you can leave all the fields displayed and disable the attachments.

12) **Click the configure box next to E-mail Address and set the Display As parameter to Email. Note the other choices. Click Close.**

13) **Click the Configure box next to Debris Type. Set the Display As option to Radio Buttons. Click Close.**

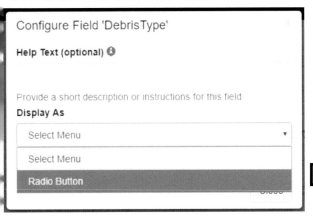

14) **Uncheck the Enable Attachments box and click Next.**

This is the fun step. There is a drop down list of style types with each producing a different color and font scheme. Look through the list before doing the next step, and choose a different one than recommended if you like.

15) **Select the Cerulean style from the drop-down list and click Next.**

On step 7 you can configure a GeoForm Viewer. This will display any submitted form with the submitted information and a map. In this scenario it would be helpful for the Public Works teams to be able to pull one up, review it, and drive to it.

16) **Leave the Disable Viewer box unchecked and change the Point Display Field to Address. Click Next.**

Step 8 has many more options for your form. One of the most important, as describe above, is the ability to work offline and load surveys when connectivity is restored. If you were setting this up for desktop use then you could disable this, but for field use you will want to leave it enable.

Read through the other options; they are pretty self-explanatory.

17 **Reading through the list of options, then press Next to accept all the defaults.**

Finally you can preview the form. Take note of these things:

◊   Some of the fields are required because when you added the fields to the new feature layer you said that these cannot be null.

◊   The E-mail Address field is formatted to take and validate e-mail addresses.

◊   The Debris Type field is a radio button display built from your pick list.

◊   The Locate Me button will read the device's GPS location and find it on the map.

◊   Step 5 has a custom title on the submit button.

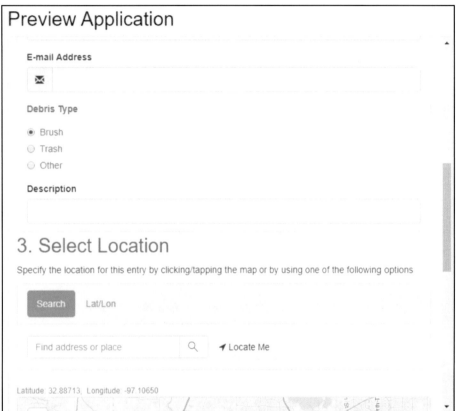

Some of these things seemed trivial at the time but remember what effect they can have on the finished form.

18 **Review the form preview, trying out the buttons and entries. Click Next.**

19 **You can use the Previous button to go back to any screen and change anything You are also able to access the Form Builder again later if you want to change anything. Click Save and Exit.**

20 **After the form builds it presents a pop-up allowing you to share the form out through your social media channels, or copy the URL.**

That was quite a ride and you now have a pretty slick GeoForm to send out after a major flood event and let people report their own issues. The wizard provided a lot of options for configuring things like helpful text and colors, and set options for attachments and other functions. The form will look good on both a desktop, tablet or phone – but you really don't have a lot of control over the final look and feel (not like what you'll see with Survey 123). Now that you know how to set one of the setup and what the final product will look like, you have a better idea of when it would be the most useful way to collect field data.

Introducing the QuickCapture App

This field app is the newest offering and is designed to be a very simple 'out the car window' data collection app.

Exercise 7b—Building a QuickCapture App

Next you will build a QuickCapture app from the other feature layers you created. Remember that this app doesn't have text fields to fill in, it just works off of pre-made pick lists and lets you make each choice appear as a "big button" in the app. The three feature layers you made earlier named CreekBottom, StormDrainOutfalls, and LargeDebris all have fields populated by pick lists and will be perfect for this. There are no fields that require anything other than picking a value from a list.

To start the creation process, go to the web page esri.com/QuickCapture (this is a shortcut to the full URL). This Overview page is a good introduction to the app as well as some links to examples. Perhaps after creating yours you can look at the gallery of other examples to get more ideas for using this app.

The Resources page has links to the mobile app, plus information on finding the app in the App Store and Google Play. This page also has a link to launch the QuickCapture designer. Note that there's also a link on the top tab bar that is accessible from any of the pages.

The designer wizard will step you through the creation process.

1 Click Launch on the Resources page, then click New Project.

Note that if you had existing projects they would be shown here and you could open and configure them. Also, if you are not already logged in to your AGOL account, you will be prompted to do so.

2 On the Search, type in Creek to make the layers easier to find. As you hover over each layer, a selection box will appear. Select the three layers you created for this app and click Next.

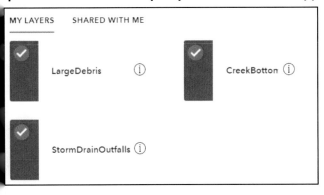

3 Title the project *Creek Inspection*, provide an e-mail address, and set the folder to *Data Collection*. Click Create.

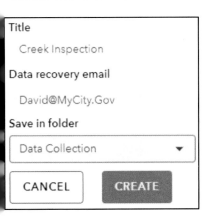

The app is created and the buttons are automatically added using the symbols you set earlier.

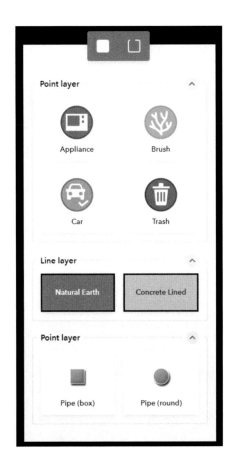

71

5 Click on the Appliance button to open the configuration panel.

The controls here are pretty straightforward. They are used to change the style of the button.

6 With the Appliance button still selected, click to add a border. Then click the Data tab in the configuration panel.

The target feature layer and the target or capture field was set automatically from the layer you chose before creating the app. If at this point, however, you decided to add buttons to populate a different layer, you could set the layer and fields here. Note that you could also collect as streaming points. When you press the button the streaming capture will start, and end the next time you press the button. The button will flash while collecting.

Because you had preset all the layers before creating the app most of these setting do not need to be changes. One thing you will change is the ability to capture a photo when this button is pressed. The photo can be required or optional, and the preview can be hidden meaning that the photo is taken when the button is pressed. Make sure your field crew knows this, however, or you'll get a lot of pictures of feet.

7 Click on the slider next to Take Photo to enable this, set as required, and set to hide the camera preview.

Copy

Delete

Change Title

Change Image

Change Size

Change Shape

Change Color

Change Border

8 One by one click the other three point layer icons in this group and set them to have a border and to have the same photo settings. This will be for Brush, Car, and Trash. Then move down to the other Point Layer group and give those buttons a border. Change their photo settings to require a photo but don't hide the preview. This will be for Pipe (box) and Pipe (round).

You may have also noticed that each set of icons had a box around it, called a group. You can change the title of the group, the number of columns it contains, the border, and control whether or not the group is collapsed when the app opens. It is not advisable to collapse a group since it will be very hard to see and open in the field, but if you have a lot of layers or layers that are only populated rarely then this might be an option.

9 Click to highlight the top Point Layer. In the configuration pane, change the title to *Large Debris – Take Photo*.

10 Rename the other two groups *Channel Type* and *Outfall Type – Take Photo*.

The app is starting to look pretty good, but the two buttons in the middle look a little plain. Rafael has made you some icons to use for the various buttons in this app, and they are located in the icons folder that came with the downloaded data. You could also design your own and save them as a .jpeg or .png or other popular file formats.

11 Click the Natural Earth button and in the configuration panel click on Image ADD. Navigate to the Icons folder in the downloaded data and select Earthen.jpg. Repeat for the second button making its image Concrete .jpg.

12 In the upper right, click Save.

Watch very quickly in the lower left while the project is saving ... a box will appear that when click will display the QR Code for the project. If you click that you can scan to open the app or copy the image to add to any instructions you might write and distribute.

13 Click the icon in the upper left [icon] to exit the QuickCapture Designer.

From this screen you can see all of your projects (you probably on have one), and if you hover over a project you can edit the configuration or view the results in a web map. Of course if you tried it now you would get a blank map since no data has been collected.

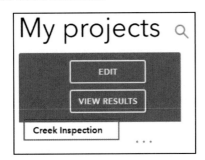

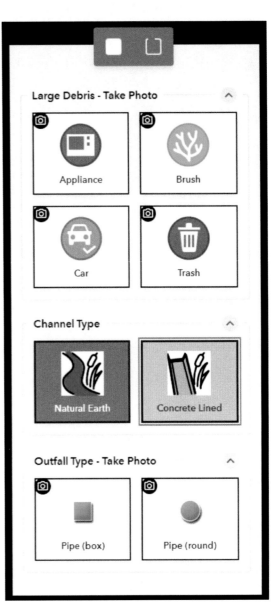

14 Close the designer page and return to your AGOL page and look in the Data Collection folder.

You can see that the item is in your Contents list and has many of the same characteristics as other items. If you share this as Public, the people running and using the app will not need a login.

15 Change the Share on the QuickCapture project to Public.

That's all there is to it.

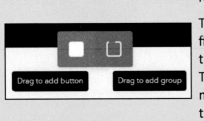

Rafael's Question – What are the two orange boxes at the top of the designer screen?

These allow you to add a new group and new buttons in case you want to manually configure another feature layer for collection. First you have to add a new group by dragging that icon down into your app screen, which you could rename and change other settings. Then you would add buttons by dragging them into the new group. You would have to manually configure which layer the buttons are attached to and set the field into which they would store data. Quite an ordeal and much more difficult than setting up your layers in advance, but it can be done!

The only thing left to do is test the app!

1 **Load the app onto your device (see the QuickCapture Resources page for file locations and assistance).**

2 **Open and log in to the app.**

RT

Recovery Team

Texas Emergency GIS Response
Team

SIGN OUT

If you like, click on the Settings screen to see the options associated with this app. You can control how often it sends data so make sure it is doing so at a rate that is appropriate. If you have it set to once an hour that may not be very good for a disaster response but may be fine for other instances.

And the fun surprise is that it can translate all your actions into speech – you have to try this out a few times before you decide to turn it off. It'll absolutely freak out the fields teams, especially if you can figure out how to make it speak French or Thai or something!

3 **Click the Plus Sign icon at the lower right** ⊕ **to find and load the new project either by browsing or scanning the QR Code.**

4 **Then click the project to run it.**

Walk it around outside and try it out! Try the Large Debris buttons which take a photo as soon as you press it, and compare that to the Outfall Type buttons that open the camera and let you preview and take a photo in a normal fashion.

Two things to note on this screen. One is the GPS accuracy shown at the bottom which is totally dependent on the type of device. If this exceeds 98 feet the app won't allow any collection. The other thing to notice is the box in the upper right. In the image above you see an orange circle with a 1 in it. This shows that there is 1 response waiting to be uploaded. Since the update frequency was set at 30 seconds, this should disappear within that time. If it doesn't, it signifies that you are not in a connected environment and responses are being held in memory until you are.

Pressing that box will open a map which will display where you are, and any line or polygon features currently being collected. It doesn't display the collected features, though.

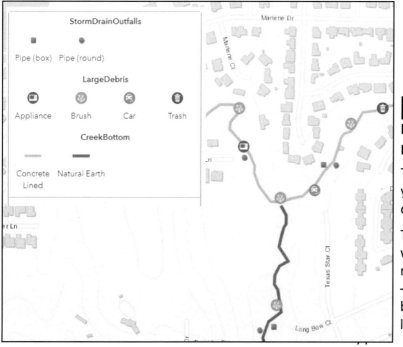

5 **Continue to collect features as a test. When you have a few dozen points and lines collected, close the projects and exit the app.**

The data is stored in the feature layers and from there you can make new web maps and web apps using that data.

The demonstrations for this show it being used out the window of a car at speed. Imagine driving down the road and taking pictures of street signs out the window – or missed garbage pick-ups - or road-kill. The possibilities are endless. Just be thorough on your feature layer set-up and the design process will be easy.

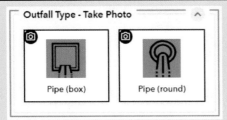

Rafael's Question – the symbols for the pipes are pretty generic, and I noticed that you have better icons in the Icon folder … can I use those?

Certainly. See if you can go back into the designer, remove the images for the Pipe (box) and Pipe (round) buttons, and replace them with the two from the Icons folder.

Using Survey 123 for Data Collection

Next up in the field data collection realm is using Survey 123. This app presents a form much like GeoForm except that it allows for pick lists, text field inputs, radio button selection, photos, and much more and is the most robust of the field data collection apps. It also allows for really tight form designs, unlike GeoForm that did a very generic layout. In Survey 123 you can set columns and boxes, change colors and fonts, and control almost every aspect of the form. Consequently it is a little harder to set-up and configure.

The basis of the Survey 123 form is the ODK XForms specification. This is an open source formatting language that can control how data is displayed in a spreadsheet environment – most commonly using Excel and the XLSForm standard. Visit the websites GetODK.github.io/XForms-Spec or XLSForm.Org for more detailed information on any of the formatting techniques.

There are several ways to create these surveys in AGOL. One way is to create them from an existing feature layer, much the same way you did with a GeoForm. And just like QuickCapture you will want to fully develop your feature layer in advance to get the most out of the form. Any pick-lists that you define will be used, and after the survey is completed you can further design the look and feel of the form.

This method is done through Esri's Survey 123 Connect program using an Excel spreadsheet. You will be able to manually code your new form, and the formatting code is pretty simple to learn. In addition, Connect displays both a spreadsheet to code in and a preview of the finished form. Changes made in the spreadsheet can be saved and previewed very easily before committing to the final version.

Exercise 7c - Making a Survey from an Existing Feature Layer

A good way to start learning about these surveys is to build one of a familiar feature layer using the automatic process, then examine the results to see how the input fields were configured and possible tweak the final product. In this exercise you will make a survey from the Denver Road Closures layer you made earlier. It will be a good idea to first go back and look at how that layer was designed to better understand the output. Also, recall that the Denver Road Closure layer was from an Esri template and may contain fields that you don't need to include in the survey.

1 Start AGOL and login to your account (if necessary).

2 Go to the Content tab and open the GIS Guidebooks – Disaster folder.

3 Find the Denver Road Closures feature layer and open the item details.

4 Click the Data tab, then click the Fields button.

There are a lot of fields in this list, but only a few of these need to be in the survey. The others could be populated later or are tracking fields to see who has edited the data. Note that they are checked here just for emphasis and them being checked does not affect the creation of the survey.

You can also examine the fields for the inclusion of a pick list. The fields Reason, Full Closure, and Active all have a pick list. These could be used in the survey, however the field Active could be calculated with an Arcade expression on-the-fly in the map so it won't need to be included.

The next thing to check is to make sure the layer is editable. The app needs to be able to add a new feature as well as update existing features, so make sure the layer has those permissions set.

5 **Move to the Settings tab and note the Editing settings. Change the settings to allow Add and Update if necessary. Save changes if needed and return to the Content tab.**

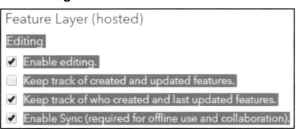

Remember, the more work you do here to prepare the layer the better your survey will turn out.

If you have not already done so, you will need to download and install Esri's Survey 123 Connect. You can find this on the Survey 123 web page.

6 **Open a web browser and go to the page Esri.com/Survey 123. This main page has a lot of information about Survey 123 along with sample projects. Note the Contact Us section at the bottom of the page … the Esri development team monitors this and will be happy to help with any problems.**

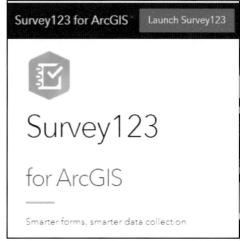

Note the Launch Survey 123 button at the top. This opens a graphic toolset where you can manually build a survey and you'll do that later. Also note the Resources tab. This is where you download the various components for different devices, see a tool reference, and work through several tutorials.

7 **Click the Resources tab, then download and install Survey 123 Connect for your device. When Completed, Open Survey 123 Connect. In the upper right, click the options button and sign in using your proper credentials.**

You will see all the other surveys you have created (if any) plus the big button to create a new survey.

8 **Click the New Survey button.**

The New Survey creation form starts with the Templates button checked. This has two stock templates that you can try out – the first has EVERYTHING that Survey 123 can do in case you want to see how something is formatted, and the second has the most commonly used, basic settings if you are just starting. The one you are about create is a good medium between these two choices.

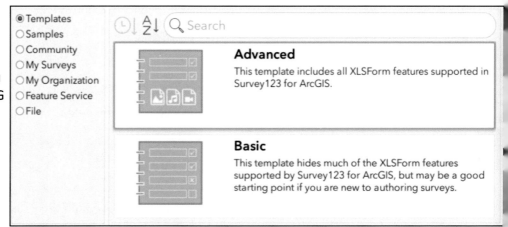

As you move down that list, you will see Samples, surveys created by Esri staff to demonstrate a particular technique; Community, surveys created by Esri and others for specific jobs which may be close to a job your are doing; My Surveys, a list of your other surveys which would allow you to make a new survey using your previous surveys as a template; My Organization, a list of surveys that were created by other members of your organization; Feature Service, which allows you to use an existing feature service as a template; and File, which lets you create a survey directly from an Excel spreadsheet you may have previously authored.

9 At the top, fill in the title Denver Road Closures.

10 Click on Feature Service. Search for Denver and select the Denver Road Closures feature layer. Then click Create Survey.

Denver Road Closures

The red lines indicate which roads have been closed as a result of the current disaster. The data contains the reason for the closure, the date it was closed, the expected date to reopen, and more. This layer can be used in a field app allowing workers to mark road closures as they find them.

Modified: Saturday, April 11, 2020 11:54:02 AM Central Daylight Time

Type: Feature Service

Owner: recovery01_TexasEGRT

Access: private

Create Survey   Cancel

After a bit, the survey will be created and two windows are opened. The left window is a preview of the survey and the right window is a spreadsheet showing the survey's coding.

You will notice that the spreadsheet has several pages. The first, called Survey, is the layout for the survey. The second, called Choices, sets up the pick lists for fields that have them. The third, called Settings, has general setting for the survey including the name of the feature layer into which the results are stored. And the final page, called Types, is a help page with descriptions of all the elements available four use in the survey. This last page is helpful if you load a survey either from a feature layer (like you did here) or from a template someone else built You can read the descriptions about the elements they used and determine

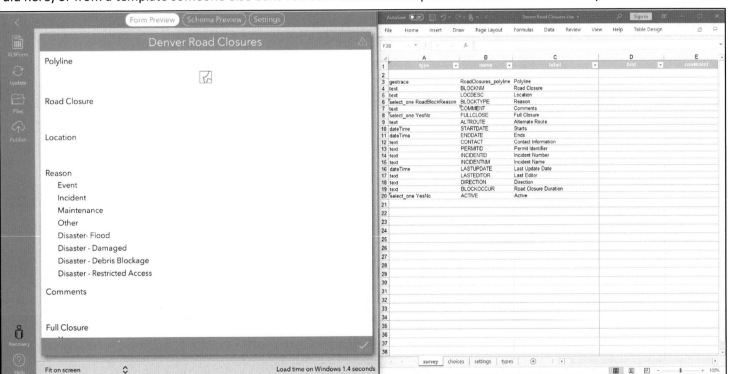

how they might be modified.

It is first helpful look at the Survey page and see what fields have been included and how they are formatted. The first three columns are the main formatting – Type identifies the format of the input controls, Name is the internal names used for the element (and cannot contain spaces or special characters, and Label is the test that will appear with the element in the survey. To the right of those columns are a few dozen columns that help configure other aspects of the formatting. Note that the first three columns are frozen so you can scroll across to the other fields without losing sight of the main three columns.

There are also hints built into the spreadsheet to help identify what function each column has. If you click in any cell the Hint will pop-up. This is especially helpful when trying to identify the purpose of the dozens of configuration columns.

Each row of the spreadsheet represents an entry box in the survey (note that these can also include some formatting tags that you will look at later), and since you created this from a features layer there is a row for each field. Notice that a new line was added at the top of the spreadsheet's Survey page – the GeoTrace type. This is what captures the geographic location – point line or polygon. In this case since the Road Closure layer is polyline, the geographic input tag is for polyline. And if you scroll out to columns U and V you will see the field type and field size for each input element. These were drawn from the layer and should not be changed!

This survey has three of the basic input types: Text, which accepts a typed text entry; dateTime, which accepts a date entry, and Select_One, which is used to present a pick list. The first two are pretty straight forward and allow the user to type in text or select a date from a pop-up calendar. The Select_One however has a unique format in the survey. In the Type column, the type formatting code Select_One is given along with a name for the picklist (which should be different than the name or label). Then on the Choices sheet the picklist is built. The lists will have the List_Name that is assigned with the Select_One formatting code, the Name (the value that is stored in the attribute table), and the Label (the test that appears as a label in the pick list). New entries for the pick list can be added simply by typing them into these three columns.

11 In the spreadsheet, examine row 6. This is the Select_One entry for the field Reason. Note the name next to the Select_One formatting code.

12 Move to the Choices sheet. Note that the List_Name matches the name in the Select_One formatting code, which is then followed by the list name and label. These were all imported from the feature layer.

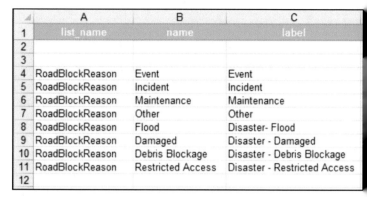

In the survey, the Reason entry is shown as a series of radio buttons. The user select one of the buttons to record the value. The Select_One can also be presented in several different appearance formats, including a horizontal row and a drop-down list. You can read about the different options on the Types sheet starting on row 38.

13 Go to the Survey sheet in the spreadsheet and using the slider bar at the bottom move the columns over until you see column I, Appearance. Click in column I on the same row as Select_one RoadBlockReason. You will see a small drop-down arrow to the right of the cell. Click the arrow and note the list of available options and click likert.

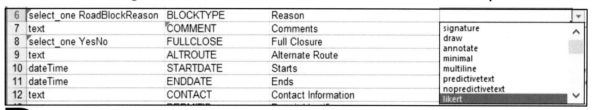

14 Save the spreadsheet. The survey preview will automatically refresh to show the new format changes. This has the pick list in a horizontal format.

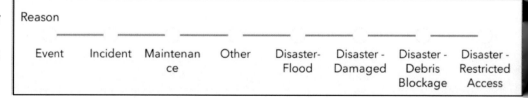

Rafael's Question – That looks bad and would be hard to use … are there other formats I can try?

Yes – although the list under Appearances on the Types sheet has many options, only some of these work with a Select_One type. If you like, go through and try the others and find one you like, making sure to save the spreadsheet after each change to refresh the survey preview.

The choices for Select_One are:

Minimal   Horizontal

(drop-down list with radio buttons)   (radio buttons are shown horizontally instead of vertically)

Autocomplete (searchable drop-down list)

Perhaps the best format for his entry is the vertical radio buttons, or the default appearance. Perhaps if the labels for the list were shorter the other appearance choices may look better.

15 **Delete the value from the Appearance column for the Select_One RoadBlockReason row and save the spreadsheet. This will set it back to the default.**

Next you can remove fields from the survey that don't need to be filled out in the field. This is easily accomplished by deleting the row for that field. Row 5 allows the user to type in a description of the location, but if this is on a map the description isn't necessary. It can be deleted. So can the fields for Last update Date and Last editor (rows 16 and 17).

16 **Highlight Row 5 on the Survey sheet and press Delete. Then highlight rows 16 and 17 and delete them as well. Save the spreadsheet.**

Note that this doesn't delete the fields from the feature layer, it only removes them from the survey. Records collected with this survey will have those fields blank. It also doesn't hurt things to have blank lines on the Survey sheet. When compiled into the survey the blank lines are ignored.

The survey is looking better and more compact, but there are still a lot of fields to fill out that may require the same value each time. Fields such as Incident Name and Incident number will always have the same value until the incident is over, and the Starts date field will almost always be today's date. Here are ways to set defaults for these that could be changed in the field for unique cases.

17 **In the survey sheet, find the row for Incident Number and scroll across to column J, default. Type in the value TD221. Then in the incident name row type in the value 2020 - Denver Flood.**

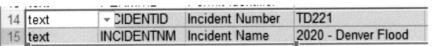

For the date, you can use the function Today() to automatically copy the system clock into the field. This would be appropriate for the Starts field but not the Ends field.

18 **In Column J for the Starts row, type in the value Today(). Save the survey.**

19 **In the survey, click the Starts field and note that it will default to the current date and time. Note also the default values you set for the Incident fields.**

That's enough for this one, so it's time to go ahead and public it and get it into the field.

 20 **In the connect screen, click the Publish button.**

You will get a reminder that the survey will be using an existing feature layer.

21 **Click Publish Survey, then click OK to complete the process. Then close the coding spreadsheet (you don't need to save it because a copy is automatically saved with the survey) and close Connect.**

That completes the building process for making a new survey from an existing feature layer. Using any of the existing Samples or Community templates, not to mention using any of your existing surveys as a template, will work exactly the same way except that they will make a new feature layer when they are published. You can always change the survey appearance for any of these options. Later in this chapter you will see how to load and run the field app, then use the survey in the field.

Creating a Survey with the Web Designer

A new way to create entry forms for Survey 123 is by using the Web Designer. This is accessed from the Survey 123 web page and allows a simple, easy to use interface for selecting and adding inputs to your survey. You can see teht the dra-and-drop interface makes it easy to visualize your completed form and is a very quick way to make a survey.

Exercise 7d—Create a Survey with the Online Tools

Next you will make a new survey from scratch using the web form on the Survey 123 page. In this scenario, you will make a survey for the bridge inspection team. After a flood, it is important to do a quick visual inspection of bridges looking for obstructions or damage and a Survey 123 app will make that process very easy. After talking with the field crew and getting an idea of what they need, Rafael designed the field layout for you.

◊ Road Name or Number – record the name of the road or highway number

◊ Guardrail Damage – Y/N recording if there is guardrail damage

◊ Pavement Condition – record the condition on a scale of Good, Fair, Poor, Impassible

◊ Structural Damage – Y/N recording if there is any apparent structural damage

◊ Structural Damage Comments – If they answer yes to the previous question, then prompt for more details.

◊ Debris – No Debris / Debris on Bridge Deck / Debris Under Bridge / Both

◊ Status – Open / Closed recording the current status of the bridge

◊ Photos – take pictures of your observations

That's eight fields plus the point location.

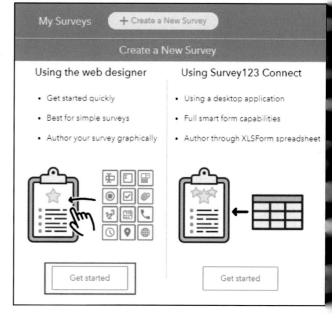

1 **Open the esri.com/Survey123 website and click launch Survey 123. Login if necessary.**

You will see the list of surveys in your account.

2 **At the top of the screen, click Create New Survey, then in the Using the web designer pane click Get started.**

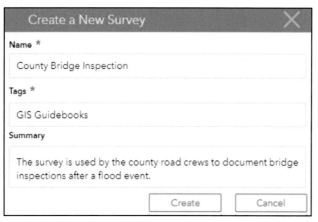

3 **Name the survey *County Bridge Inspection* with the tag GIS Guidebooks and a summary describing the project. Then click Create.**

The web designer has a survey design canvas on the left, and a configuration pane on the right. By default it will display a menu of available elements to put into the survey. You build the survey by dragging an element onto the design canvas then configuring it.

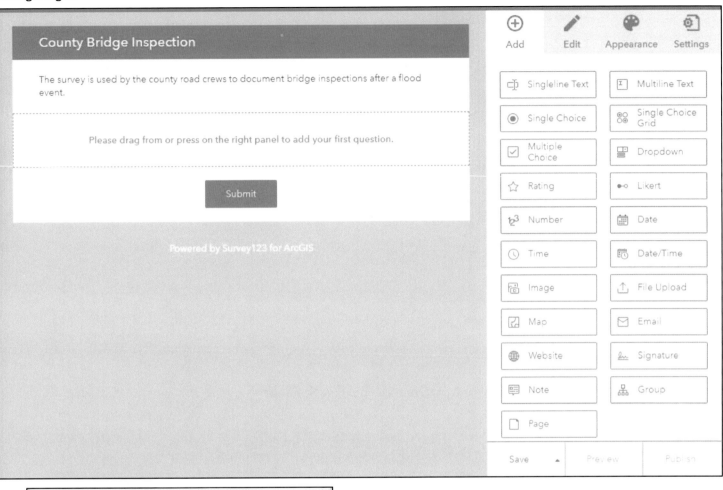

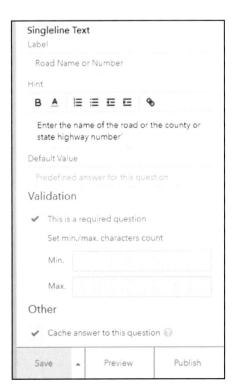

You will start by dragging in a text input for the Road Name or Number field.

4 **Click and hold on the Singleline Text box and drag it into the survey design canvas.**

The question is added to the survey and a configuration box is opened on the right.

5 **Add the label Road Name or Number and the hint 'Enter the name of the road or the county or state highway number'.**

6 **Set the Validation to be Required and check the Cache Answer box. Then click Save.**

The Cache Answer box will carry over the value as the default to the next survey. This could save time if the inspector is inspecting all the bridges on a particular road since he wouldn't have to enter the name again until he moved to another road.

The next field, Guardrail Damage, will be a Single Choice element with a pick list.

7 Click the Add button at the top of the configuration pane. Then drag the Single Choice element to the design canvas and drop it below the Road name element.

8 In the configuration pane, add the label, a hint (optional), and fill in the choices of Yes and No.

9 Use the Minus button next to the third option to remove it. Check the circle next to No, which will make it the default.

10 Try the different Appearance options and select the one you think looks best. Leave the other options unchecked.

The next field is Pavement Condition, another pick list with the choices of Good, Fair, Poor, Impassible. See if you can do this one on your own.

11 Add the element to the design pane and configure the pick list. Set Good as the default. Note that clicking the Plus button will add more choices to the list.

Now you need to add the field for Structural Damage. The layout is exactly the same as the Guardrail Damage element except for the title, so you can copy that one in the design canvas and drag it to the bottom of the list.

12 In the survey design canvas, highlight the Guardrail Damage element and in the lower right click Duplicate.

13 Drag the copy to the bottom of the canvas, then update the Label and Hint.

The field Structural Damage Comments is next, and it is contingent on the answer to the previous question being Yes. If the answer is No, then there is no reason to display this question. This is set as a rule with the element. First add the new text element, then configure the rule.

14 Add a new text element to the bottom of the canvas for Structural Damage Comments.

15 Select the Structural Damage (Yes/No) element. In the lower right click the Set Rule button.

16 Use the drop-down boxes to set the condition to If YES Show 5. Structural Damage Comments. Then click OK.

Note: It's a good idea to periodically save your project in case it crashes or the browser is accidently closed. If you have to come back to a survey that isn't published it will appear as a draft and allow you to enter the designer again.

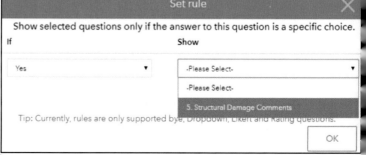

One element you can add here is a formatting element that will visually group questions together. This has no effect on how the questions operate or the values they return, but is a visual guide to the user. You drop a Group element onto the design canvas, then drag questions into it that will be included in the group. You can also collapse a group in the form, meaning that only the group name will be visible by default, but expanding the group will reveal the questions. This might be appropriate for optional questions for which the answers are likely to be unknown in the field. As an example, when doing damage assessment the owner name and contact info is typically in a close group element since the owner may not be at the property when the survey team comes through. If they are, however, the group can be expanded and that additional information collected.

17 **From the Add tab, drag the Group element onto the design canvas and drop it above the Structural Damage question. Give it a title Structural Inspection. Note the option to make the group collapsed by default.**

18 **Next, drag the two questions about structural inspections into the group element.**

Again, this serves no purpose except to visually separate these two questions from the others.

The next two inputs, Debris and Status, are pick list entries, and you've done a few of those. See if you can add these on your own. If not, refer back to the second element for hints.

19 **Add the Debris and Status pick lists.**

Next is to add the element to allow a photo to be taken. This element works a little differently than in a Connect designed survey, which you'll see later, in that it only allows for one photo. The element also allows for images to be used from the devices internal storage, or to activate the camera and collect a new image. Obviously for this you will want to activate the camera.

20 **From the Add tab, drag the Image element to the bottom of the design canvas. Set a Label and hint.**

Using this web designer, you can't repeat an element – so to get more than one photo you would have to copy the photo element. For this practice, make one additional element for taking a photo.

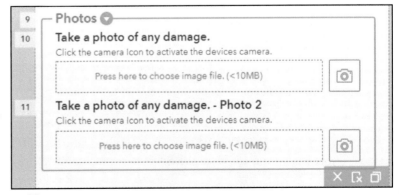

21 **Duplicate the Image element and change the label to reflect that this is the second photo.**

22 **Drag a new Group element into the design canvas, name it *Photos,* and drag the two photo capture elements into it.**

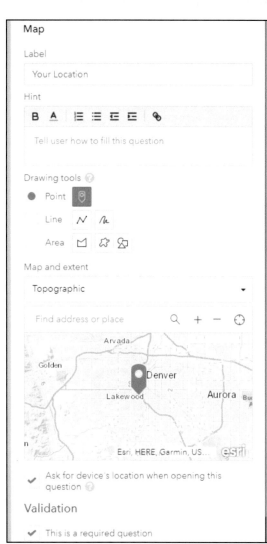

Lastly, you will add the Map element, which will store the location of the device. You can set the type of element to draw (point, line, or poly), select a basemap, and predefine a default extent. Also by checking the box 'Ask for device's location' the survey will automatically use the user's current location.

23 Drag the map element to the bottom of the design canvas. In the configuration pane, set the title to Your Location. Select the Topographic base map and check the box 'Ask for device's location". If you like, zoom the extent preview to Denver. Finally, mark the question as required. This will assure that a location is gathered.

24 Save the project.

25 At the bottom of the configuration pane, select Preview. This will show what the survey will look like in the field. Try clicking a few of the buttons, including the down arrow by the group names. At the bottom is the map that will capture the current location. Using the buttons at the top right, you can preview for different formats, too.

26 When you are finished examining the preview, click the X in the upper right to close the preview window.

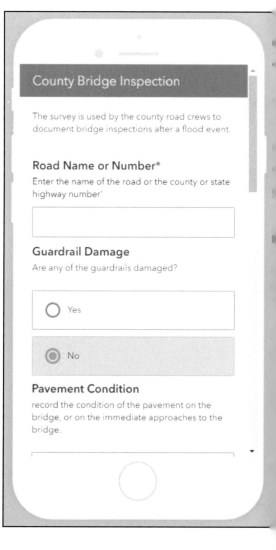

27 Finally, click Publish in the lower right corner. After a few tips and warnings, you can click Publish again to finalize the survey.

28 Next click the Collaboration button at the top of the designer along with the Submitter tab at the right to see the Share options for people wanting to use this survey and submit to this layer. This is a graphic interface for the Share options from AOGL, so you should already be familiar with them. Set sharing to Members of my organization and click Save. Note that the Link area will give a link to use this survey through a web browser, and a link to a scannable QR Code.

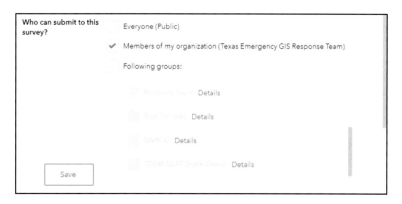

29 Now click the Viewer tab at the left. This will allow a read-only layer to be shared with the public, but this layer cannot be altered with the survey. Click Everyone and then click Save. Note that after clicking Save the links will display at the top.

30 **When done, close the webpage.**

Again, this finishes the survey. At any time you can go back into the design page and make alterations to the survey options, but be aware that deleting any questions may affect the information already collected.

Rafael's Challenge – Rafael wants to make a map of all the emergency service clinics in his area. So he wants to create a Survey 123 project that clinic owners can use to record information about their clinics, then have a public facing page where the public fan review and find clinics near them.

Think about what information might be collected – Clinic name, hours of operation, services offered, phone number, website, accept insurance payments, and physician on call (Y/N). Can you think of any others?

Make a survey to collect the information and maybe even let them take a photo of the staff or the front of the store. The QR code could be used in a flyer or e-mail sent to all the clinics. Then make a public facing page that will display the collected store information. The web link could be provided to local citizens through various channels to help them find a clinic when necessary.

Making Surveys with 123 Connect

The final part of this chapter will be to make a new survey from an existing design template in Survey 123. This template, called FEMA ATC-45 Rapid Assessment-Modified.xlsx is based on the FEMA Rapid Damage Assessment form. Texas EGRT staff have made some slight changes to the form to provide the required FEMA information along with other important information for damage assessment. The goal is to have one survey that can capture all the information to satisfy multiple agencies, thus preventing teams from either running two surveys simultaneously, or having a separate team return to the locations again. Plus with modifications made by Texas EGRT the survey will provide an assessed value of damage for each survey. The advantage here is that as soon as the field staff completes the survey a damage value is calculated. Back in the Emergency Operations center (EOC) a dashboard can display a running total. When the last survey is completed, the total value of the damage is immediately known.

You will make a new survey using this modified ATC-45, then examine the setting in the spreadsheet to better understand how portions of the form were made.

In addition to the modified ATC-45 spreadsheet, other spreadsheets along with supporting documentation was included with the book's datasets in a folder called Survey 123. Several of the documents are editable Word documents with instructions for using the various surveys. You can use this to write custom instructions for any surveys you build based on these materials.

Exercise 7e - Make an ATC-45 Survey Using an XLSX File

You saw earlier how to start Survey 123 and select a source for the survey. In this scenario you will make a new survey and create a new ATC-45 Modified survey. This is the survey most commonly used by Texas EGRT for damage assessments.

1 **Start Survey 123 Connect and log in to your account.**

2 **Name the survey ATC-45 Corsicana (or you can use the name of the city you are in).**

3 **In the list of design sources, click File. Then click Browse for XLSForm and navigate to the location where you installed the book's materials, and open the Survey 123 folder.**

4 **Select the file FEMA ATC-45 Rapid Assessment Form – Modified.xlsx and click Open. Then click Create Survey.**

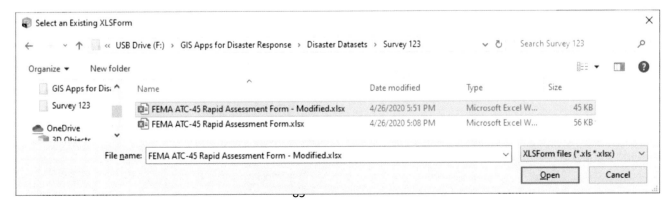

The survey will open the preview screen and the spreadsheet. At the lower left of the screen is a pop-open menu that will let you change the format of the preview. This will give you an idea of what the survey will look like on different devices as you design it.

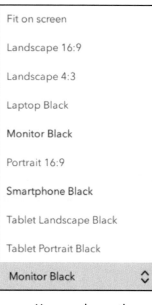

First you will interact with the survey to see some special formatting, then you will take a look at the spreadsheet to see how that formatting was accomplished. Notice in the preview that there are many groups, and in the spreadsheet each one is color coded so that you can tell what falls within each group. You learned before that groups are only for visual control and to make things appear more organized to the user, and the colors are only for the benefit of the designer and do not affect the survey in any way.

Start at the top of the preview and examine, then interact with each of the inputs. Then check the spreadsheet to see how that was accomplished.

5 The top row is Site Address and is an unmodified text entry box. Type in *1234 N Main St*

6 The next item is a collapsed group item called Building Information. If you click the arrow at the left it will open the group to display three standard text entry boxes.

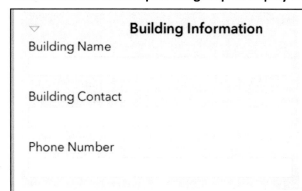

Note the grey color of the box outlining the group. You can leave them blank.

In the spreadsheet you can see that the group was started by putting 'begin group' in the Type column. The group is ended by putting 'end group' in the Type column, and every row between these two codes are included in the group. Then the 'compact' code was added to the Appearance column which means the group will be collapsed by default when the app opens. Note also the HTML formatting tags to center the title in the form.

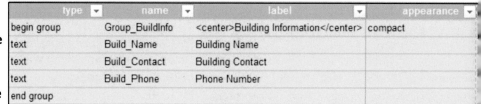

type	name	label	appearance
begin group	Group_BuildInfo	\<center>Building Information\</center>	compact
text	Build_Name	Building Name	
text	Build_Contact	Building Contact	
text	Build_Phone	Phone Number	
end group			

7 Next, in the preview area click in the Number of Stories entry. A numeric keypad will open allowing entry to be done from this keypad rather than opening the device's keyboard. Set this value to *2*.

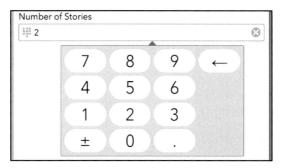

This is coded with the standard 'integer' code in the Type column. The inclusion of the 'numbers' code in the Appearance column causes a keypad to open rather than rely on the device's keyboard. Note also that the default is set to 1 in the Default column.

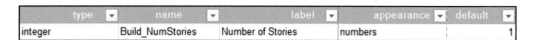

type	name	label	appearance	default
integer	Build_NumStories	Number of Stories	numbers	1

The next field is really unique in that it pops open a calculator. It is set to capture square footage and the teams that had been using this form would estimate the length and width of the building, then open a calculator app and calculate the square footage. By having the calculator embedded in the form it saves them time.

The result of any calculation will be used as the entry for this field. The calculator also has memory functions built in, so for ell-shaped buildings you could calculate a portion of the building, click M+, then calculate the rest and click M+. Clicking MR would recall the value and enter it as the input for the field.

8 **Click the Footprint Area line in the form and a calculator will pop up. Enter 55 x 45 and click Equals(=). Note the red star next to the title indicating that this is a required field.**

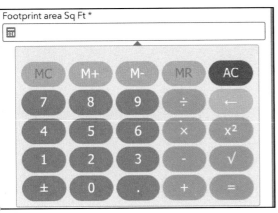

The code for the calculator po-up is done using 'integer' in the Type column and the code 'calculator' in the Appearance column. The entry is set to be required by adding the word 'yes' in the Required column.

type	name	label	required	d	appearance
integer	Build_SqFt	Footprint area Sq Ft	yes		calculator

Next up is another group names Group_BuildType. You will recognize this by the use of the 'begin group' and 'end group' codes in the type field. This group is set to be open when the app runs since there is nothing in the Appearance column. But there are some interesting things happening in this group. The first question is a pick list, and the next questions are dependent on the answer to the first question. Depending on your choice a second question (or no question) will be presented. This is done by writing an expression in the Relevant column.

9 **In the Type of Building group, click each of the answers and note the change in the next question. After you have clicked them all at least once, finish by clicking One or two family dwelling. Leave the second question at its default value of 1. Again note that this entry is required.**

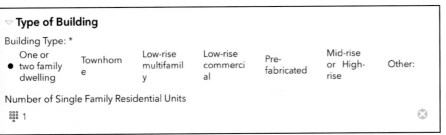

To understand how this entry works you should look at the Building Type entry and see how to build the picklist. The display of the values in the form is exactly the same as when you built the survey with the web tool, but with a special code to handle the option of 'Other'.

You see in the spreadsheet the Type is set to 'select_one', followed by a name for the pick list you will create, followed by the code 'or_other'. This name should be different that the element's name and label. Then the Appearance is set to 'horizontal' to create the radio buttons across the page, and finally there is a default value of One/Two_Family.

10 **Try selecting the Other choice and note what happens.**

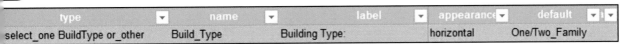

type	name	label	appearance	default		
select_one BuildType or_other	Build_Type	Building Type:	horizontal	One/Two_Family		

11 **Move to the Choices sheet and look for the List_name BuildType.**

This is the same name that followed the 'select_one' code. There is a row for each choice you wish to include in the list. The row has the List_name, Name (the value stored in the attribute table), and a Label (the text shown in the selection list. But notice that there is no choice for Other.

The 'or_other' code automatically adds the ability for the user to type a response into the same field that the pick list is populating without having it in the pick list. This keeps from adding a special field for 'other', but note that this option is not available in the web form designer.

It's easy to add more rows to the spreadsheet for

list_name	name	label	image
BuildType	One/Two_Family	One or two family dwelling	
BuildType	Townhome	Townhome	
BuildType	Multifamily	Low-rise multifamily	
BuildType	Commercial	Low-rise commercial	
BuildType	Prefab	Pre-fabricated	
BuildType	Mid/High	Mid-rise or High-rise	

more selection, or even delete rows from the pick list. Changes to the list do not affect the basic structure of the dataset so they can be changed after the survey has been published. Note also the Image column which will let you add an image to your buttons, much like you did in the web designer. There's even an 'image-map' Type that uses a SVG image for your selections – too much to cover here so search the web for "Survey123 Work with SVG file".

So what is controlling the visibility of the second question? First you must have all the available questions in the spreadsheet. Then you build an expression that can equate to True or False in the Relevant column. The express should contain a field name bracketed with a ${}, then an operator (such as >, =, <=), followed by a value. The value can be anything, and using numbers are pretty easy – but in the case of text it is best to use a picklist in the source field so that you don't get tripped up by typos. In this instance two of the questions differ in that they ask for a count of single or multi-family dwelling units, and each value is stored in its own field. Both of these questions have an expression controlling when they get displayed.

In the spreadsheet, note the two questions in the Building Type group coded as 'integer'. Then you see the code 'numbers' in the Appearance column, followed by the expressions in the Relevant column.

type	name	label	required	d	appearance	default			relevant	
integer	Build_NumMFUnits	Number of Multi-family Residential Units			numbers				${Build_Type} = 'Multifamily'	
integer	Build_NumSFUnits	Number of Single Family Residential Units			numbers	1			${Build_Type} = 'One/Two_Family' or ${Build_Type} = 'Townhome'	
end group										

The first expression is formatted like this:

${FieldName} operator ValueName

or

${Build_Type} = 'Multifamily'

Note that the FieldName comes from the Name column of the controlling question and the ValueName come from the Name column of the pick list. The choice from the original question is evaluated against the pick list and if the expression is True then the new question item is displayed. If it is false, then the question item is not displayed. The second question is relevant for two of the choices from the picklist, so an OR connector is used to add a second expression. A list of available operators is on the Types sheet. In this example only one of the additional questions would be displayed, but in fact any number of questions could be displayed for a particular question. For instance if the original question is answered Multi-Family then the survey could ask two addition questions, one for number of units and one for the range of apartment numbers.

The next group for Primary Occupancy is pretty straight forward, using codes you've already seen.

12 **Try clicking several of the answers from the Occupancy Type list. Do any have an additional question pop-up, and how is that being controlled?**

13 **Examine the next question – Is there standing water? Is it in a group? How is the pick list built? Does it have a relevant question linked with an expression, and what would that expression look like? Note that the default answer is keeping the relevant question from displaying.**

Those input questions all used code items that you have seen already. This next group has a few new things. The first is a 'note' type. This is strictly text that is displayed in the form that requires no interaction from the user, nor does it accept any input or store any value. Many times these lines will have additional HTML formatting to give the survey a richer look and feel – although it should be noted that any value in the Label column can have HTML formatting code with it.

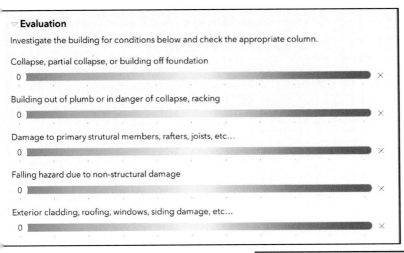

After the 'note' item are five questions where the user rates the condition suggested by the label on a scale of 1 to 10. These use an 'integer' Type paired with a mysterious Appearance code called 'distress', which we believe was meant to record a patient's pain level. It has a preset scale and color palette that creates a horizontal slider bar with a green to red color palette and allows for numbers between 1 and 10.

14 **Try moving the slider bars for the questions, setting them in order to 5, 6, 7, 8, and 9.**

15 Next check the codes in the spreadsheet. Note the use of the 'distress' code in the Appearance column as well as the default value of 0.

type	name	label	d	appearance	default
begin group	Group_Eval	Evaluation			
note	Group_Note	Investigate the building for conditions below and check the appropriate column.			
integer	Eval_Collapse	Collapse, partial collapse, or building off foundation		distress	0
integer	Eval_Plumb	Building out of plumb or in danger of collapse, racking		distress	0
integer	Eval_Structure	Damage to primary strutural members, rafters, joists, etc…		distress	0
integer	Eval_FallHaz	Falling hazard due to non-structural damage		distress	0
integer	Eval_Cladding	Exterior cladding, roofing, windows, siding damage, etc…		distress	0
end group					

Rafael's question – I like the distress bar, but is there a way to customize this to a wider range and with different colors?

Yes, but not as the 'integer' code. Instead use the 'range' code in the Type column, and this can be configured for both decimals and integer input. Then check to see if your survey has columns called 'parameters' and 'body::esri:style' (and if not, just add new columns and name them this in the first row). In the parameters columns you set the start value, end value, and step value. In the body::esri:style column you set the startColor, endColor, and background color. Examples with the configuration codes above them would be:

A few things to note:

◊ Don't put any spaces around the equal signs or between color names

◊ The last example started at a negative number, had a default of 0, and the dot started in the middle of the bar

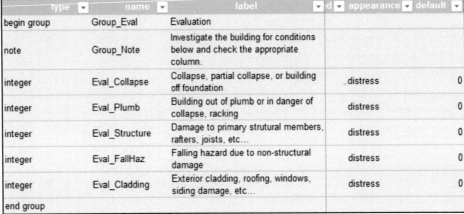

◊ The last style parameter 'color=' is the color that is revealed when you move the slider. Omitting this value makes the covering color transparent so that the background colors don't change when the slider is advanced.

◊ If you use a color name the designer code doesn't recognize it will default to black. All the color names can be found at https://htmlcolorcodes.com/color-names/

◊ The colors can also be noted as a hexadecimal value (https://htmlcolorcodes.com/color-picker/)

◊ If you use an Appearance code of 'no-ticks' the slider won't display the tick marks or the high/low values.

In the first example moving the slider dot doesn't change the color, and in the middle example the slider dot moves to reveal yellow. If you're brave enough, try configuring the five distress bars using the range code. Hint: the first example in the image above will be very close to the default look and feel.

This is also where the form begins to deviate from the standard FEMA form. The question about exterior cladding etc... is important information to have in doing the final assessments of the buildings. A damaged solid brick wall is structurally different than a wood framed wall with the exterior cladding blown off.

Next is another area that differs from the FEMA form. You see two questions; Estimated Building Damage in 5% increments, and the five standard FEMA Damage Categories. In the emergency management world, the Emergency Management Coordinators need to have the damage categorized by the five FEMA categories because they need that for the required FEMA reports. The percent damage for each category is this:

◊ Less than 5% damage – No Damage

◊ Between 5% and 10% - Affected

◊ Between 10% and 30% - Minor Damage

◊ Between 30% and 65% - Major Damage

◊ Over 65% - Destroyed

However, for estimating the cost of the damage and more precise scale is needed. After all, the difference in the value of 30% damage and 65% damage is very large, but these percentages fall into the same FEMA category. So EGRT has modified the form to ask for percent damage in 5% increment – then the form will automatically select the corresponding FEMA category. This is done by putting a series of IF statements in the Calculation column of the FEMA Category item. The IF statements determine what was chosen in the percent damage item, then uses that value to determine the FEMA category. If the team going into the field is not comfortable using the percent damage scale, then can ignore that and just click the FEMA categories directly – but the percent damage will stay at 0%.

16 Try clicking the various percentage values and watch the FEMA category change. Note – once you click the FMEA category manually the automatic calculations will no longer work. Make your last click on 45%.

Estimated Building Damage

| 0% | 5% | 10% | 15% | 20% | 25% | 30% | 35% | 40% | 45% | 50% | 55% | 60% | 65% | 70% | 75% | 80% | 85% | 90% | 95% | 100% |

FEMA Damage Category
No Damage
Affected
Minor Damage
● Major Damage
Destroyed

Next is the Location item. This will record the location of the device as either a point (geopoint), a line (geotrace), or a polygon (geoshape). The line and polygon types require more interaction with the survey to start and stop the collection of the geographic item. If using the geopoint the location is stored automatically. Several things to note here – one is that the accuracy of the features collected are dependent on the accuracy of the device you are using. Most devices have a 30 to 50 foot accuracy (or worse), but you can add a GPS location enhancer to the device and the survey will use the more accurate location value. The second thing to note is that the location is stored when you first click the 'Start New Survey' button. So it's OK to stand at the house to start a new survey, then wander around the property collecting the rest of the data.

There's not much to see in either the survey preview or the spreadsheet so a quick glance will show how these are set up.

The next group called Placard records the type of placard left and the warnings written on the placard. This section is used when the building officials make the structural survey to assess if the building can be entered. All of the components here are familiar by now, having been used earlier in other surveys you've done.

The next item is the one that lets the user take one or more photos. You recall that when you added the photo button to a survey using the web designer you had to add one button for the number of photos you wished the user to take. In this instance, there is one button, but the user can advance the roll to take more. This is very efficient because it doesn't take up as much room in the displayed form and the web-designed survey did. Allowing multiple photos is done through adding a 'begin repeat' code in the Type column. This is capped with an 'end repeat' code and everything in between is repeated. There is a Repeat Count column into which you can specify how many times this section should repeat – and in this case it represents how many photos you want to allow.

17 Note the Damage Photos section in the preview screen. The user is presented with the option of taking a photo with the camera, or using a photo already on the device. The slider bar at the bottom allows you to move to a new photo capture screen, and in this instance take up to 5 photos. Take a photo or upload a file from the device, then advance to the second photo.

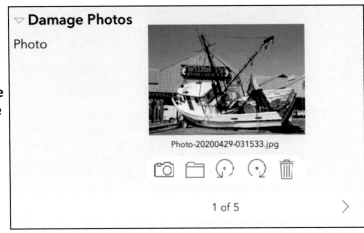

18 The code for the repeat is very similar. Scroll the sheet far to the right and look for the Repeat Count column (not shown in the graphic below).

type ▾	name ▾	label ▾
begin repeat	Repeat_DamagePhotos	Damage Photos
image	Photo	Photo

There are also some interesting things that can be done with the 'image' Type code. If you set the Appearance column to 'signature' the survey opens a special box into which you can sign your name. And setting Appearance to 'draw' will let you draw in a sketch or diagram. While not used in this survey you could try them in your next sample survey to see how they function.

There are a few other questions that are similar to others you have already seen and you will no doubt recognize how they are coded. There is a new format, however, in the Inspection Date/Time item. This field will capture the current date and time using the constant 'now()' in the Default column.

Note the Inspection Date/Time entry field. It is populated with the date and time of when the survey was started. Although it can be changed manually, there is no reason to ... just leave it alone.

Inspection Date/Time
📅 Tuesday, April 28, 2020   🕐 9:36 PM ⊗

19 Check the code in the spreadsheet. You will see that the Type is 'dateTime' and the Default is 'now()'. There is also a time function called Today() that can be used as well.

type ▾	name ▾	label ▾	·d ▾	appearance ▾	default ▾
dateTime	Insp_DateTime	Inspection Date/Time			now()

This type of date field will allow the user to change the date if they want, and that might be useful if someone is adding surveys from the desktop after the fact. But there are two codes that will capture a date and time with no interaction from the user, and in fact do not even display in the survey. They are 'start' and 'end'. These are best used when you don't want the user to change the date, or perhaps in addition to the user definable date time if you also wanted to get the actual time and perhaps subtract the two to get the elapsed time it took to fill in the survey.

An interesting code and formatting combination is getting just month and year with a Date code; If you put the code 'date' in the Type column and set the appearance to Year, you get the current year with + and − buttons to increase or decrease the year. Or make the appearance Month-Year and you get two boxes with the increase and decrease buttons. Not super helpful in disaster response but a cool thing to know.

The next group has a special formatting to make the selections look more like a table, but still use radio buttons. The formatting code 'table-list' goes in the Appearance column on the same line as the 'begin group' code. This affects all the questions in the group, and they all have to be 'select_one' type and use the same pick list. Then all the choices will be lined up on a grid.

A good example might be asking several customer experience questions with the ratings Poor, Fair, Good, Great, and Fantastic (and this example even used the 'or_other' code).

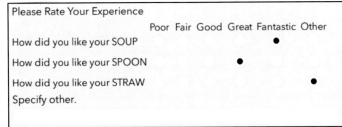

Please Rate Your Experience

	Poor	Fair	Good	Great	Fantastic	Other
How did you like your SOUP					●	
How did you like your SPOON				●		
How did you like your STRAW						●
Specify other.						

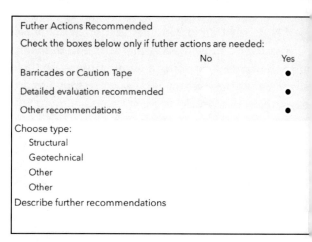

Futher Actions Recommended

Check the boxes below only if futher actions are needed:

	No	Yes
Barricades or Caution Tape		●
Detailed evaluation recommended		●
Other recommendations		●

Choose type:
   Structural
   Geotechnical
   Other
   Other
Describe further recommendations

20 **Scroll down to the Further Actions Recommended group and try the radio buttons. Do any trigger a relevant question?**

Turns out that two of the questions have a relevant question, but note in the code below that those two questions must appear outside the table-list formatted group.

21 **Check the formatting code in the spreadsheet dealing with the table-list group.**

type	name	label	appearance	default		relevant
begin group	Group_Actions	Futher Actions Recommended	table-list			
note	Actions_Note	Check the boxes below only if futher actions are needed:				
select_one yes_no	Action_Barricade	Barricades or Caution Tape		no		
select_one yes_no	Action_Detailed	Detailed evaluation recommended		no		
select_one yes_no	Action_OtherRec	Other recommendations		no		
end group						
select_one ActionDetailed_or_other	Action_Type	Choose type:				${Action_Detailed} = 'yes'
text	Action_Other2	Describe further recommendations	multiline			${Action_OtherRec} = 'yes'

You now find yourself at the last question, which is the Damage Value field. There are several questions throughout the survey that are required: Square Footage, Building Type, and Percent Damage. If these are populated, then the Damage Value field will automatically figure out the value of the damage using a pre-set dollar-per-square-foot multiplier. The numbers used are standards from the building industry, but you can tweak these if necessary for your area.

23 **Check the Damage Value field. It should have a calculated value – if not go back and check the entries for square footage, building type, and percent damage.**

Check the Calculation column for the field entry to see the formula (it's too long to show here).

Damage Value

139219

The advantage to calculating on-the-fly is that, as stated before, the total value of damage is known as soon as the last survey is completed.

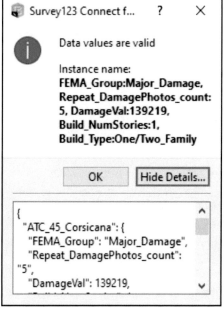

Survey123 Connect f... ? ✕

Data values are valid

Instance name:
FEMA_Group:Major_Damage,
Repeat_DamagePhotos_count:
5, DamageVal:139219,
Build_NumStories:1,
Build_Type:One/Two_Family

OK   Hide Details...

```
{
  "ATC_45_Corsicana": {
    "FEMA_Group": "Major_Damage",
    "Repeat_DamagePhotos_count":
"5",
    "DamageVal": 139219,
```

24 **Finally, click the Check at the bottom of the survey. At the disaster site this is used to submit a survey, but while designing a survey it is used to validate all your entries. If there are any issues they will be detailed in the pop-up box.**

It took a bit of time to get through all that (and a lot of pages in the book), but this survey is a great learning example because of the variety of formatting options used.

25 **If everything checks out OK, click the Publish button to complete the survey. Once this is done the survey is ready to be used in the field.**

26 **When the publishing process completes, close Survey 123.**

If you want to test the new survey, load it onto a device and take it outside. Then try filling in the form and taking photos. Any issues such as misspelled words or the addition of more choices can be easily made in the designer, then published again. Publishing over an existing survey will not destroy the data. You do need to be careful, though, of not changing the data structure. Deleting an entry in the survey will delete the data from that entry in any surveys that have been completed, but adding an entry will make those fields blank in the existing data.

Rafael's Challenge – The Incident Commander has an idea for a data collection task and has asked Rafael to help. The power company wants a street light inventory for a tornado disaster area. Streetlights are not metered, they are connected straight into the power grid, so if one is damage it will prevent them from reestablishing power to the area. They want Rafael to drive around and look for all street lights and record the information in the form below:

Location: _____

Type of pole: (Wooden Pole) (Metal Pole) (Other ... describe) _____

Type of Fixture: (MH) (HPS) (LPS) (MV) (LED) (Other)

Is Fixture Broken:

(No)

     (Yes) – Globe is broken or missing / support arm is damaged / fixture torn loose / wiring is damaged

          (circle all that apply)

Take a photo (up to 4)

The Location can be a geopoint – the Type of pole, Type of fixture, and Fixture Broken questions can be pick lists, and if a fixture is broken have a "select_multi" question open about extent of damage - Then take some photos.

To get fancy, you could add a Description field just below Type of Fixture and fill this in automatically depending on which fixture type is chosen (and add the or_other code):

MV = Mercury Vapor

HPS = High Pressure Sodium

LPS = Low Pressure Sodium

MH = Metal Halide

LED = Light Emitting Diode

Exercise 7f - Optional options

There are a lot of addition options and settings besides the default configuration that can be set for your surveys. In disaster response, we typically stick with the defaults because there may be teams waiting to start their field work while we are building this and you don't want to hold them up while you are tweaking colors and such. If you would like to take a look at these, follow through the instructions below.

1 **Open Survey 123 Connect and log in. Then open the ATC-45 Corsicana survey (or whatever you called yours). At the top of the screen, click the Settings button. Note the row of buttons that will appear below the Settings button.**

The General tab will allow you to change the title, summary, or description of the survey. This is pretty straightforward, just like practically any item in AGOL.

2 **Add the Summary "Modified ATC-45 Rapid Assessment Survey", and fill in a more detailed description.**

The Style tab allows you to restyle the screen colors. This can include the text, background, toolbars, and input prompts. You can also apply an image to the background but this becomes highly distractive and may make the survey harder to read, so be careful if you do this.

To change a color you can either type in a color name, type in a hexadecimal value, or click on the Default box and select from an interactive color palette. Remember that you can look up color names at https://htmlcolorcodes.com/color-names/. On the other hand, setting them by hex number is the most precise. But most people will select from the interactive color palette. Note that if you type in a color name it doesn't recognize it will set the color to black.

Click the Style tab. Set the Text Color to #661605 and the Background Color to Light Green. Then experiment with the other color selectors, trying different methods until you have a color scheme you like.

Next the Map tab will let you set the default map extent for the survey. The GPS unit in your device will set the location for you, and adding the data to a map later will automatically zoom to the data extents. It defaults to the Esri campus in Redlands, CA, but you can change it if you like.

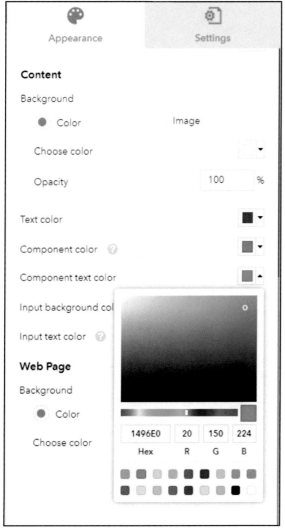

The Images tab controls how large of an image the survey will capture. You can set these small to reduce the amount of data transfer needed with each survey, or higher if you need hi-res images. Setting it to Unrestricted will use the device's default settings and is usually pretty high. If volunteers are conducting the survey with their personal phones, make sure they know the data requirements so that they don't go over their data plans.

Skip over the Inbox tab because it'll come up later.

The Sent Surveys tab has a setting to enable saving the surveys on the local device (default). You can turn this off if you are doing a crowd source survey or something very informal and casual where losing a couple of surveys here and there won't matter. But DO NOT turn this off if you are doing damage assessment after a disaster. It is important to have a way to retrieve any surveys that you think did not get transmitted to the server.

And finally the Linked Content tab identifies the feature layer associated with this survey. If you were making a survey from scratch and needed to use a specific feature layer you might manually set this. Otherwise it's best to let the survey create its own feature layer.

Note that for these settings to go into effect, you would need to republish the survey. After reviewing all the tabs, close Survey 123.

In the Survey 123 Web Designer page, you can click the Appearance tab to control the same things. You can set colors by hexadecimal or using the interactive color palette.

Future projects for Texas EGRT

We are constantly battling the idea that different agencies have to send workers into the field to do their own damage assessments, going to the same houses and pretty much asking the same questions. First a search and rescue team has to go house by house, recording the address, owner information, type of structure – then a CERT team goes to the same houses and asks the same questions, along with the FEMA categories, depth of water, or high water mark - then a relief agency comes through – then the building officials team comes through – then the FEMA team comes through. By the time the last group comes by the home owners, who are having a pretty lousy day, are fed up with answering the same questions over and over. So EGRT has designed a version of the modified ATC-45 with the questions grouped by who will be asking them and controlling the visibility. This is controlled by asking at the top of the survey which agency you are with, then putting a Relevant statement to show only the questions that this agency needs to ask. When the next team goes out they can open up existing surveys and all the basic information from the first group is populated, leaving them to concentrate on only the questions pertaining to their agency. By setting the default on the first question to the agency before they go out, they will only see their agency's questions – but the groups are only collapsed so if they do get information for another agency's questions they can expand the group and fill it in. The last team out will have most of the questions already filled in and can concentrate on the few remaining questions – and in our case it's usually the building officials doing a structural assessment. This means that the first team gets the basic info, and all the rest of the teams have "follow-up" questions.

That's where the mysterious Inbox tab comes in to play. With this option active the user will be able to scroll through or search existing surveys, then open and edit them. A sample of this type of survey is in the data that came with the book, in the Survey 123 folder. The file is called ATC-45_Multi_Agency.xlsx. We haven't been able to get all the agencies to cooperate on this yet, but the time will come when this is the norm.

Rafael's Question – how do I decide which app to use?

The answer is going to depend on the type and conditions under which the data is to be collected, and the sophistication of the group doing the collection. If this is going to be a quick drive by assessment from the street, the QuickCapture or a basic web designed Survey 123 app might be best. If this will involve a long and complicated form used by an expert team, then Survey 123 Connect might be the best interface for designing the form. The important thing is to discuss the project with the team going into the field and find out exactly what data they need to collect – and sometimes you can suggest things that they can collect while they are on-site to help other agencies. Just make sure your survey collects everything it can to prevent repeated trips to the site. I know of a neighboring city that sent field crews out to collect and build a sign inventory. When they were done, the boss said, "OK, now can you tell me what kind of poles the signs are on?". D'oh!

Chapter 8 – Creating Web Apps

Web App Creation Methods

All the efforts into creating, collecting, symbolizing, configuring, and mapping the data is the lead up to building a great web app to display the results. The app may merely display data, or it can include tools and widgets to let the viewer interact with the map. When you were making web maps, you were careful to make the map contain the data you needed for a specific purpose, symbolize it to display the data a certain way, label it for best effect, and create pop-ups to provide a visual display of addition data about each feature. All this work needs to be showcased or enhanced when it is placed in an app.

Before making an app you always want to understand how it will be used and what type of information the viewer will want to get from it – this will guide you in determining how you will make the app, which map to include, and what widgets you may need to include. If this is intended to be an editing interface, make sure that the app has the appropriate tools for adding or updating features. If it is intended to be an analysis map, then certain analysis widgets will need to be included and configured. Or perhaps it is a view-only map that does not allow for user interaction. Whatever the case, decide the purpose of the app before beginning.

There are just a few ways to make a web app in AGOL, but each of these ways has dozens of possibilities giving you an almost unlimited array of ways to customize your apps. You can start with the Configurable Apps, which are a group of premade templates. Your web map will be placed into the template and you have the option to preview a live version of the app. Don't like it? Simple go back and pick a different one. If it is what you want, simply clicking Create Web App will build the app into your AGOL account.

The advantage of the templates is that rather complex apps can be made even if you don't know a lot about programming them. For instance, the Imagery Viewer is a very complex template and would be hard to build yourself – but the templates gets you up and running in no time. You can get information on all these templates in the online documentation. Find this by doing a web search on 'Esri Configurable App Templates". For each template there is a full page of instructions and examples.

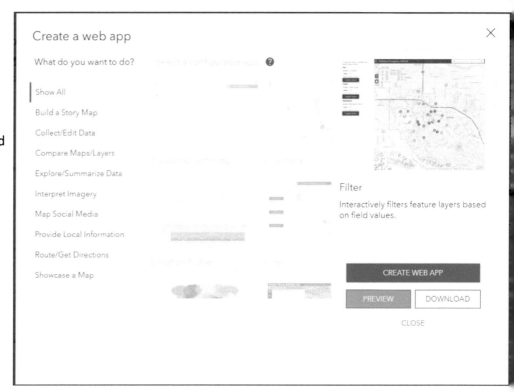

One drawback of the premade templates is that you are limited on customizing the individual template. The tools included in the template are the ones you get and you aren't able to add or remove tools and widgets. However if you are a programmer and are running your own portal it is possible to download the source code for any of the templates and modify it as you see fit.

Another easy-to-use method of making web apps is to use the Story Maps wizard. As the name implies, this isn't just for making a web app but for making a full story around your maps. This will build a web page with titles, text, images, maps, and who knows what all. The wizard steps you through creating the story which can be as long or short as you want. After making the basic start to the story, you can add in more text, more maps, more images, and even embed other web pages.

The story is laid out in one continuous page that the user scrolls down. And although a lot of interaction with the contents of the web page can be added, the maps are view-only maps. It would be possible, though, to embed a web app with maps and controls into a story. Tehese type of story maps aren't intended for use to edit or update data, and not for field apps. It might be useful for a briefing atlas or for documenting a series of maps done during a disaster for a post-incident review, but remember that the viewer must see the maps in sequence and it's difficult to jump to a particular map.

The most versatile of the methods is the Web AppBuilder. As the name implies it does indeed build web apps, but more specifically map based web apps. The map is the main focus of the app, and you don't have the ability to add side bars, video windows, rich text boxes, or many of the niceties of a story map. They are intended to be the working map, suitable for editing, field apps, analysis projects, and much more. The creation process is fairly simple – provide a title, tags, and summary and the basic framework is created. The configuration stage, however, can take hours and hours because of the almost limitless combinations of themes and widgets.

Esri Configurable Apps

When you get ready to make a web app, there are two ways (and probably more) to start. One is to click the Create button and select the type you want, and the other is to start from a web map's Item Details page and select the Create Web App button. Both have the same choices of creation method but by starting in a web map's Item Details page you will start with a web map already in the app and allow you to preview the template with your actual data before building the app. Otherwise you have to specifically add a web map to the app – or perhaps you want to build the app using a web page URL.

Exercise 8a - Using Premade Templates

As an easy start you will make an app from one of the premade templates. These are easy and fast to create, and in a disaster that works in your favor. Early on in this book you created a simple web app for the Austin Area map. That map had the typical layer controls and the zoom/pan functions but little else. Which points out the value of seeing what tools are available in a template before selecting it as the one to use.

In this scenario you will make a web app using the web map Daytime Population – Workers vs Residents. The users won't need to edit the info (and in fact they can't) but still want to have normal mapping tools like turning layers on and off and zooming/panning. They may also want to filter the data to show only specific features within the data. You can look through the available templates and see what might be suitable.

1 Start ArcGIS Online and log in (if necessary). Click the Content tab.

2 Open the GIS Guidebooks – Disaster folder and find the Daytime Population web map you made previously. Open its Item Details.

3 Click the Create Web App button and select Configurable Apps.

4 Browse through the apps, looking specifically at the purpose and category of each. As you click and read the purpose of the templates, click Preview and play with a few. Check the online help also to read more about the configurations of each. See if there are any you think will be good.

As you try a few, you will find that this web map doesn't have the data to support some of the templates. For instance, none of the templates that use imagery will work because this map has no imagery. The editing templates aren't appropriate because this map contains Living Atlas data that you cannot edit. Some of the Explore/Summary templates work well, as do the simple viewer templates. Rafael likes the Summary Viewer template, so that's the one you'll do here. But later on you can try some of the others on your own.

5 In the 'Create a Web App' dialog, click the Explore/Summarize Data category and select Summary Viewer.

6 Then click Create Web App.

7 Enter the title *Daytime Population Summary Web App*. Leave the Summary blank and it will default to the same as the web map. Click Done.

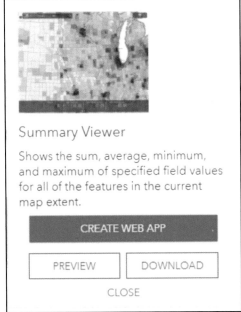

Summary Viewer

Shows the sum, average, minimum, and maximum of specified field values for all of the features in the current map extent.

CREATE WEB APP

PREVIEW   DOWNLOAD

CLOSE

When it has been built, the web app will open. The typical template will have several configuration tabs on the left plus Save, Launch, and Close buttons at the bottom. The General layer lets you define the web map(s) to use, and this one chose the Daytime Population because you started at this map's Item Details. If you had started the creation process without first selecting a web map, this would be empty and you could set it now. Or if you wanted to change the web map being used, this is where to change it.

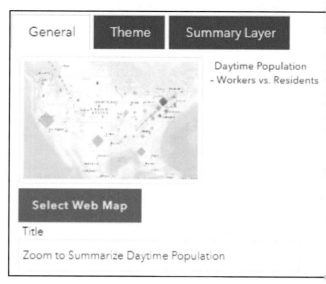

8 On the General tab, change the Title to **Zoom to Summarize Daytime Population**. Then click Save.

9 Move to the Theme tab. For this exercise you won't change anything but just examine the options here.

This tab typically lets you select the colors used in the app, and sometimes allows the selection of different layouts (ie. where to put the title and map controls in the screen display). This example also has a place to enter a URL to a custom logo.

10 Click the Summary Layer tab.

In this particular web app, the last tab lets you set which feature layer, and which fields, to use in the summary. It is preset to allow five fields plus a spot to show the number of features being displayed. Each of the different templates will have different configurations. It would be impossible to show and demonstrate each of them but you can examine the app, try a few settings, and begin to understand the settings. The app is using the layer for states as the default, meaning that you will get summaries for entire states. It would be better to summarize by Census tract.

11 Change the Summary layer to **USA_Daytime_Popualtion_2016-Tracts**. Then click Save.

You can preview the settings you make in the display next to the configuration menu, but to see the true results you can use the Launch button to open the app in a new browser tab.

12 Click the Launch button. Zoom in to an area and watch the display change. Note that the summary won't display until you are zoomed in far enough for the layer to become visible.

In this app you don't really control the area being summarized, it summarizes by what's visible in the map extent. If you wanted to summarize by something else, like city, and the city wasn't a perfect rectangle you would need to use a different app.

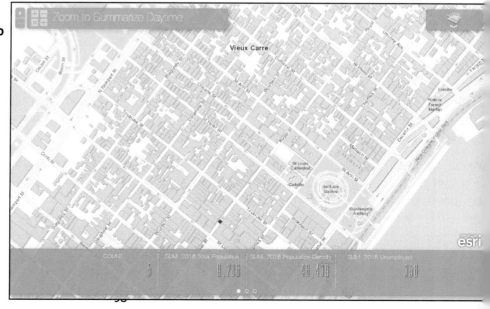

13 **Close the app window, then click the Close button. This will take you to the app's Item Details page.**

From the details page you can view or configure the app, update the metadata, or set the share parameters. If you scroll down to the bottom right you will see the URL for the app. This can be sent to others that want to use the app, or used to embed the app in another page.

14 **Return to the Contents tab and close AGOL if you aren't continuing.**

Rafael's Challenge

Earlier in the book you made a web map called FtWorth_PW_Management Map. The EOC has now asked if you can make a desktop editing screen for that.

They would like the Planning Section Chief to be able to draw in areas and assign them to different task forces from his tablet at the command post. Open the item details of the feature layer, select Create Web App > Configurable Apps, and see which one you would use for this. You can stop here and preview a few if you like, then move on to see if you agree with Rafael's choice.

Knowing that this would have to include an editing task, Rafael looked mostly in the Collect/Edit Data category. After previewing a few he settled on using the Edit template. Go back and preview that one (if you didn't already) and see if you agree. Then build a web app using the Edit template. Choose a title, color, and other parameters and test the functionality by drawing in some team assignments.

In this case, the edit tool conflicts with the pop-ups, so you will need to go back to the

feature layer and disable the pop-ups for all the layers. Once you exit the creation process, you get back to the configuration screen by opening the app's Item Details page and clicking the Configure App button. Note – if you chose a different app template, go ahead and build it, too, and see how it compares with Rafael's choice.

You see that using the pre-made templates is a quick way to build an interesting web app, and these have a large array of good functionality. If you find the exact configuration to meet your needs then you are all set. But what if you don't? What if there's one that has functionality that you like but you also want other widgets and tools? In that case you should look at the Web App Builder.

The Web AppBuilder

As explained earlier the Web Appbuilder lets you select the maps to include in an app, select the theme, and select tools and widgets to include in the app. There's still no programming involved but you will need to be comfortable configuring the widgets. Some of these get a little involved, and some are very specific to a certain type of data, and many more are ones that you probably work with every day. By combining these components you are building a fully custom web app simply by dragging and dropping or pointing and clicking. You can do these without writing a single line of code. Of course there's always the option to download a page you've configured and doing further customization on your owner server.

The best way to start with a custom Web Appbuilder app is to sketch out what you want the app to accomplish, and specifically what tools you want to present to the user. For example, do you want the user to be able to turn layers on or off – or see a legend when the app opens – or edit certain data in the app – or capture bookmarks – or find features near your location – or query the data based on a selection – or on and on and on. A complete list of widgets can be found in the online help by doing a web search for 'Esri Widgets Overview'.

One you know the purpose of your app, you can begin to build it. You can set colors, the layout, what areas to display, and add widgets. Then you can start making the app user friendly by providing documentation and instructions. Take a step back and imagine that you are not a GIS expert – would you be able to intuitively use the app, do you need instructions, and is it providing the information you intended? The better you are at accommodating these things, the more successful your app will be.

Exercise 8b – Build an App with Web AppBuilder

Rafael has an idea for an app using the Covid-19 Count by County web map you made earlier. This one is going to be very simple as a start. The app will display the web map and add a tool so that the user can search for a particular county. He also wants an information panel that the user can pop open and read about the source of the information. It's a simple app, but will be a good example of configuring the Web AppBuilder.

1 **Start AGOL and go to the Content tab (if necessary). Find the Daily Covid-19 Count by Count web map and open the Item Details.**

2 **Click Create Web App and select Web AppBuilder.**

3 **Provide a title of "Daily Covid-19 Count by County Web App", add a summary, and click OK.**

The builder interface opens with a sample display of the app and a configuration window at the left. The first tab is Theme. You can see thumbnails of the available themes and below that are the Style choices and the Layout choices. By clicking a thumbnail you can preview it in the display. The differences in the themes concerns the location and size of the title bar, the placement of widget buttons (in the title bar or free floating), the inclusion of a border, as well as some other subtle difference. The online help has a list of the themes with an explanation of their differences, but previewing them will give you a good idea of their look and feel.

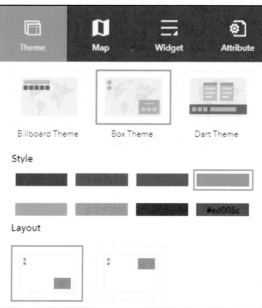

The Layout selections at the bottom can control where in a theme the free floating widgets and the title bar will appear. And the Style choices set the color of the theme, with several pre-set choices and an option to enter a custom color. There are lots of choices from simple to complex and many variations of each theme.

For this app you can use the Box Theme because of its simplicity.

4 **Click the Box Theme thumbnail. Set the Style to the turquoise color and leave the Layout at the default choice of putting the title block at the bottom right.**

5 **Click the Map tab.**

The web map that you chose for this app is shown, but if you had created an app without selecting a map you could set it here. But the most important thing you set here is the extents and scales.

Under Set Initial Extent you have the choice of using the extents of the current view You set it right now and hit save) or using the web map's default extent (this was set the last time the web map was saved). ALWAYS use the first option. Zoom the display to what looks right and set it. Otherwise you may have the issue with someone going into the web map to tweak some small item and inadvertently saving the map with an extent zoomed up to something. If you set it here then you are assured of consistency for all users.

The other often overlooked setting is the visible scales. This isn't the same as you worked with in the web maps where you decide when a layer turns on and off – this is the amount of zooming you allow in the map. As an example, if you were showing data summarized by state, zooming to the multi-continent scale is rather pointless. Conversely zooming to the street level wouldn't show any more data than zooming to the state level. With the Customize Visible Scales settings you can keep the viewer from zooming out too far or too close.

When you click the Customize button to see the available scales, the numbers you see are obtained from the caching levels of the base map. If you are using a stock Esri base map they are all cached at the same levels. But if you are using a custom base map with caching levels you set, you would see those listed. Why is this important? If you set a view scale that is not one of the base map cache levels, the base map will not show at that level.

For this map you will want caching levels that don't allow the user to zoom out past the state of Texas or in pas the county viewing level.

6 In the Customize Visible Scales area click **Customize**. **Select and delete all the values above 9,244,648 and below 288,895.**

7 Click OK and save the app.

Rafael's Question – How can I tell what levels to delete on my own maps?

Unfortunately there is no scale display to help with this. But here is a way to determine which scales to delete. First zoom the map using the – (zoom out) tool as far as it will go. This is the world view from space. Then start clicking the + (zoom in) tool until you reach the zoom level you want, keeping count of how many times you click the tool. You may have to pan to your area of interest, but only use the zoom in tool for zooming. However many times you clicked the tool, that's how many values to remove from the top of the list. Once that is set, start at the full zoom again (using your reduced level) and using the zoom in tool click until you get to the view level you want, counting the clicks. That's how many MORE levels you want below the top level. If you click six times, then you will have a total of seven levels. Go back to the customize list, count from the top the number of levels to save, and delete everything below that. If you mess up, there's a reset button at the top and you can start all over.

---

8 Click the Widget tab.

Widgets are little programs that put tools into your app. Each has a function and unique configuration settings, and it would be impossible to give examples of ever widget. Each widget has a link to the documentation page explaining how to configure it but you are on your own to decide which widgets to include in your app and when.

In this theme there are a selection of widgets pre-set to go into the display area of the app. Different themes treat these differently, though, so you will have to see if the tools will appear in the display or in the title bar. For this theme there an option at the top to add other widgets to the title bar. Rafael wants a search tool, and there is one that is preset to appear in the display but he feels that it would be best in this case if the tool was in the title bar.

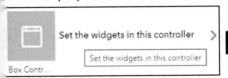

9 Click in the 'Set the widgets in this controller' box to get the list of widgets.

There are currently two widgets in the title (or controller) box. —>

Clicking the plus sign will open the selection dialog for all the other widgets.

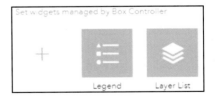

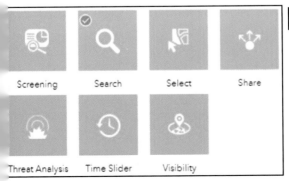

10 Click the Plus sign. In the display, scroll through and find the Search widget. Click it – a little check mark appears. Note that you can search for a widget name at the top, and select multiple widgets to add at a time. Click OK.

By default the Search tool wants to use the Esri World Geocoder and find addresses. In this instance you want to only allow searches by county name. This is done by adding a search layer and identifying which field to search.

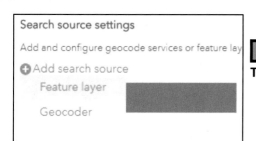

11 Hover the cursor over the Esri World Geocoder and click the X to delete it. Then hover over Add Search Source and click Feature Layer.

12 Select the layer to use (there's only one in this map) and click OK.

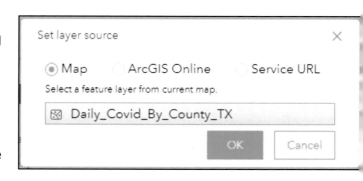

13 At the top of the box, set the widget name to *Search by County Name* (this is what displays as a tool tip). Then set the Placeholder text to *Enter County Name*, and set both the Search and Display fields to Name. Click OK and save the app.

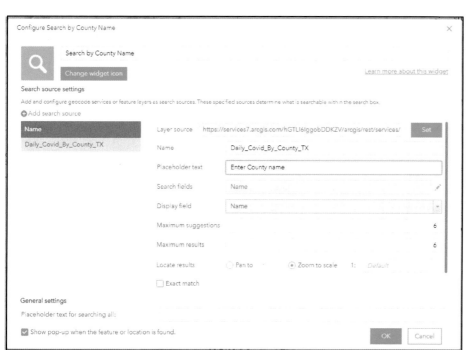

Note that there is a second place under General Settings for placeholder text. This would be used if you had multiple search sources set and wanted the prompt to reflect both of them. For instance, if you had a search source for the World Geocoder and a Zip Code layer, you might want the placeholder text (which is the prompt in the search box) to read "Enter address or Zip code".

As soon as the widgets are added, they are active and can be tested.

14 Hover over the search tool and note the tool zip. Then click the tool to see the placeholder prompt. Click in the entry box and slowly type Croc – the suggestion pop-up will provide county names as you type. When you see Crockett, click on it. The map zooms, Crocket County is selected, and the pop-up box opens. When you are done, click the Options box to return to the title bar.

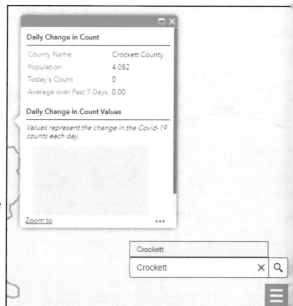

That's pretty much doing exactly what Rafael wanted, but after looking at the county info there should be a way to return to the full view. One of the preset widgets for this theme has that functionality.

15 In the Widget tab, click the back arrow to return to the initial configuration pane. Find the Home widget and click the icon in the upper right corner of the icon – tooltip Show this widget. Save the app.

The widget is added below the Zoom In / Zoom Out tools.

16 Click the Home tool to test it.

One last thing. When the map zoomed to Crockett County, it would be nice to give the user an idea of where in the state this county falls. There are 254 counties in Texas and sometimes it's hard to know where each one is. Again, there is an Overview widget in the preset list.

17 Find the Overview widget and click its Show This Widget button. Click the pencil button (configure this icon) if you like, but the default settings for this widget are fine. Save the app.

18 Try the process again – search and zoom to Panola County. Note the pop-up and the display in the overall map. Close the search tool and use the Home tool to return to the full extents.

Rafael's initial idea was fine, but these two additional widgets make the app much more usable and user friendly. He also wanted an information button to display information about the data used in this app. That can be done with the About widget, which is not one of the preset widgets.

The next steps give an overview of adding that widget, but try on your own first.

19 In the Widgets tab, click in the 'Set the Widgets' area, then click the plus sign to add a new widget.

20 Search for or locate the About icon and click it. Click OK, then fill in some metadata about the app.

21 Click OK, then return to the Widget tab. Save the app and test the new About tool.

The last tab is the Attribute tab. The top section deals with branding, for example adding a logo, title and subtitle, and link to a website. This particular theme doesn't allow for a custom logo.

The last settings in this tab are advanced and for particular widgets and uses that will not be demonstrated here. For future you might read the help topics on these settings in case you need to deploy them.

22 Save the app.

Now you will want to get a feel for what the app will look like to the user. You've tested the functionality in the display, but you also need to see what things will look like in a web browser (without the configuration pane) or on phones, tables, and other mobile devices.

At the bottom of the Configuration pane is a button called Launch. Clicking that will open the app as seen by the user in a web browser.

23 Click the Launch button. A new window will open and show the app. Try finding a few counties such as Bexar or Freestone. Close the window when done.

24 Next click the Previews button. Select one of the phone or tablet templates and note the appearance of the app. In the upper right corner you can switch the app from portrait to landscape. Try locating a few counties such as Jones or Reagan.

You will find that different mobile devices will show and control the tools differently so it's always a good idea to test on actual devices as well as the previews. Note also the QR Code in the corner. This can be copy/pasted into instruction sheets where it can be scanned to load the app. You can also get the URL for the app from the item Details page. Of course you will want to set permissions before sharing the app (password protected or public?).

25 **Return to the Configure pane, save the app (if necessary) and return to the Content tab.**

26 **If you are not continuing, you can edit AGOL.**

Your completed app has all the style and functionality of any of the premade templates, and even better it is exactly tailored to your specific need. And unlike the premade templates, if your needs change later on you can go back and reconfigure the app to have more widgets, different tools, and more! You could even download the source code and use the Web AppBuilder Developer's Edition and do even more customizing to the app (but that's a whole new book!).

Exercise 8c – The Situational Awareness Widget

Here's an actual case that Raffie worked on involving bed counts for nursing homes and assisted living facilities. The State of Texas wanted to do an inspection for a purpose we won't name here of every nursing home and assisted living facility in the state. They built task forces that would mobilize in an area, schedule appointments, and visit each facility. The data is easy – the HIFLD data has a nursing homes layer that is easily accessed. But they wanted to be able to draw a polygon on a map and get a list of all the nursing homes within it (a count as well as a list of contact info). There's a widget for that called Situational Awareness. Go look it up in the help docs. The user can set a point or line and select features within a distance, or draw a polygon and select features within the polygon. You will use the second action to do a summary of bed counts and produce a list of facilities. All of these steps you've done before except configuring the Situational Awareness widget, so minimal instruction will be given up to that point.

1 **Open ArcGIS Online and login (if necessary).**

2 **Open the Esri Living Atlas website (LivingAtlas.arcgis.com) in a new browser page. Search for Nursing Homes and locate the HIFLD data of the same name. Then at the far right click the Options button and select Map Viewer to open this data in a new Map.**

	Nursing Homes		Type	Contributor		⊕ ☆ ⋯
	This feature class/shapefile contains nursing and assisted care facilities for the		⊕ Feature Layer	kiersten.hudson_geoplatform		
	Homeland Infrastructure Foundation-Level Data (HIFLD) database				Map Viewer	
	(https://gii.dhs.gov/HIFLD)				Scene Viewer	Nursing Homes
Public Health					ArcGIS Desktop	

3 **Set a filter to show only the State of Texas (State is 'TX'). Change the icon if you like.**

4 **Save the map as "Nursing Homes Web Map" with appropriate tags and a summary.**

5 **Open the new layer's Item Details page, then click Create Web App and select Web AppBuilder.**

6 **Provide an appropriate title, tags, and summary then click OK.**

7 **Select a theme – this tool will add a box across the bottom so pick a theme with the tools shown across the top of the screen. Select a style and layout. It's usually a good idea to select a theme color that is different than the symbology being used in the map.**

8 **Move to the Map tab and set the Initial Extent and customize the scale if you wish. The lower end of the zoom scale should be close enough to see block level streets.**

9 **Go to the Attributes tab and set the branding if you like. Save the app before moving on.**

10 **Depending on the theme you chose, the new widget could go in a couple of different places. Decide, then select the location and click the Plus icon to add a new widget.**

11 **From the list click the Situation Awareness widget, then click OK to add to the app.**

Situation Aw...

Now comes the interesting part, configuring this widget. When the tool is used, a display window will be opened along the bottom of the display. At the left will be a set of selection tools and across the rest of the windows will be individual tabs, each displaying summary information that you set up. In this case you want to show the summary of the number of beds (one tab) and a list of nursing homes with their contact information (another tab). So you will need to add two tabs.

What you see in the initial widget configuration window are the general setting for the widget. You can keep the defaults here and perhaps tweak them later. For now, concentrate on adding the two tabs.

12 Click the Add Tab button. The layer is already set because there's only one.

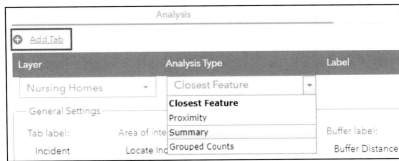

The analysis type can be one of four choices:

◇ *Closest Features* – returns the single closest feature to the items you draw

◇ *Proximity* – returns a list of all features within the aera you specify (either with a polygon or by buffering a point or line)

◇ *Summary* – summarizes field values for the features within the area you specify

◇ *Grouped Counts* – returns a count of features categorized by a field you specify

For the first tab you will do a summary on the field containing the bed count.

13 Set the Analysis Type to Summary, then add a label *Total Bed Count*.

14 Under Actions, select Edit.

Note that you can only show five summary fields in the results bar, so choose wisely. In this dataset, only the Bed Count field is consistently populated. The others are sporadically filled so they should not be trusted in a summary operation.

15 Set the first field to Beds with the label *Total Beds* and the Type of Sum. Under Actions click Edit and check Modify Field Values, setting them to round to zero decimals. Click OK.

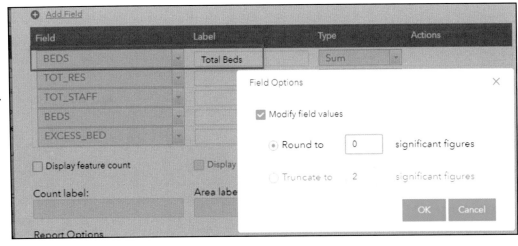

16 Delete each of the other four fields (click Delete under Actions).

17 Check Display Feature Count and set the label to *Count of Facilities*. Click OK.

That finishes the configuration of the first tab ... so on to tab 2.

18 Click Add tab. Set the Analysis Type to proximity and the label to "List of facilities".

19 Click the Edit button. You will note that only three fields can be shown.

20 Set the three fields to *NAME*, *ADDRESS*, and *TELEPHONE*. There's no need to display a feature count since the first tab is doing that. Click OK.

Field		Label
NAME	▼	Name:
ADDRESS	▼	Address:
TELEPHONE	▼	Phone Number:

Rafael's Question – You could only show three fields, does that mean if you export the list only those three fields will get exported?

No, in the Output tab you can see the choice of exporting all the fields, only the three you chose, or the fields configured in the pop-up. Maybe you should check that one, then go back and configure the popup so that all the empty fields don't get exported?

~~Change any other setting you like, then click OK. Save the app.~~

21 To test the app zoom up to an area, then click the Polygon tool. Draw a polygon in the map, double click to complete
22 it. The results will display at the bottom. In this example, the target area has 7 facilities and 209 beds. You can also click the second tab to see the list.

Click the second tab to see the list.
23 Note that if you click a number in the list the map will pan to it. Also note the download button.

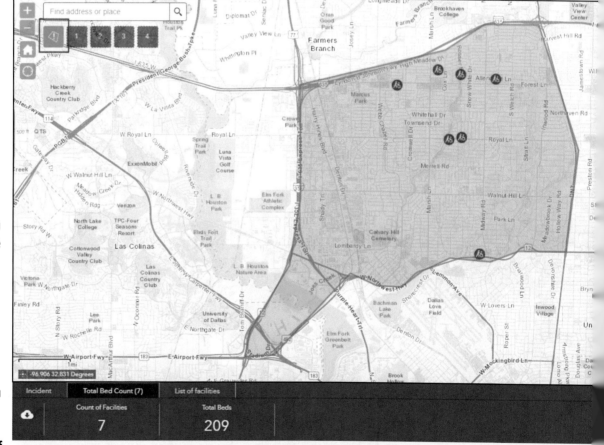

For an extra challenge, see if you
24 can add a third tab that will show a count of each type of facility using the TYPE field.

Use the Launch or different formats. You
Previews buttons to try out the app in will find that this widget is only suitable for

25 desktop or tablet use; the phone screens are too small. Perhaps in testing you will find some other widgets that you will want to add.

Save the app and return to the Content tab. If you are not continuing, exit AGOL.

26 You saw that there are many widgets that can be added to the Web AppBuilder apps, many that you may see and use on maps every day and some that would require more research in order to implement them successfully. These exercises should give you a good idea of what it makes to configure an app and how to research and install various widgets.

Chapter 9—Operations Dashboards

One of the newest, and probably most instantly successful web app templates is the Dashboard template. You may have noticed a Dashboard theme in Web AppBuilder, but that theme is a bit limited. It would be OK for a simple dashboard but once you learn how to use the Operations Dashboard builder you won't want to use that theme but rather design your own each time. Many of the ArcGIS Solutions also come with a pre-made dashboard specific to the solution. You can certainly jumpstart your dashboard creation this way, but it will also be helpful to know how to configure the dashboards in case any part of your application varies from the pre-made solution – or if you want to modify the template.

If you have seen the news or any web site dedicated to the Covid-19 pandemic, then you have no doubt seen an Esri Dashboard. These are relatively easy to configure and super informative, especially to the non-map crowd. They can include a map, but also provide on-the-fly data views such as counts, charts, lists, and more. This also means that only feature layers with lots of data in addition to location are suitable for dashboards, so when designing layers make sure you include and populate all the fields you may want to display later.

A quick web search on Operations Dashboard Examples will yield dozens of examples in a variety of disciplines. You may even find some that don' even have a map! That's because many of the dashboard elements can draw their data from a table, and do require a map for their purpose. Scanning through the examples will give you an idea of what can be done with dashboards, as well as provide some design inspiration for your own dashboard.

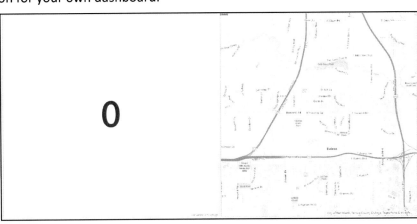

Dashboard layout

Laying out a dashboard is a little tricky because it's total open to your ideas. Elements such as the map will want to be large open panes to make them readable, but elements such as charts or feature counts can be much smaller. To achieve this they are often stacked in columns or lined up in rows, otherwise you get a large pane with one number in it and a lot of blankspace.

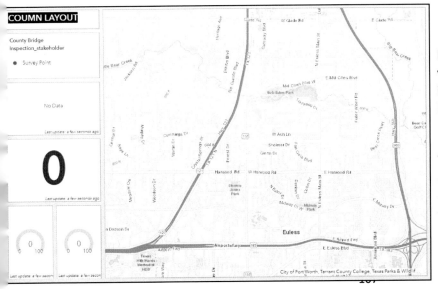

But by stacking elements and making columns you can take back much of the blank space giving it to the map and making the dashboard read better.

You might even make the map smaller and concentrate on the data displays if the intended audience is not that interested in the map. That's totally up to you, and as you see there is an endless number of ways to layout the elements in your dashboards.

There are many different elements that can be added to a dashboard ranging from fairly simple to very complex. Three of the simple ones, and ones that will be used in the first exercise, are the Indicator, the Gauge, and the List. The Indicator element basically displays a number, and that number can be a statistic using one of the layer's fields (such as a count or sum) or even a calculated value using an Arcade expression such as a percentage or change rate.

The Gauge element shows a circular graphic and can indicate how much of something there is relative to a total. Picture a gas gauge showing how much fuel is in the tank relative to full, or in other words showing where the 10 gallon mark is relative to the 24 gallon full volume. But these can be any numbers that are relative in quantity such as shelter occupancy vs. capacity or number of inspections completed vs. the total number to perform.

And the List element is just what it says – a lit of features from the database. The features can be filtered and sorted, and you can choose which fields from the features you display. For instance the list may be filtered to only active flood gauges and show only the ten with the highest value. This lets the user scan the data rather than scan the locations on the map.

Exercise 9a - Building a Dashboard

In this exercise you will build a dashboard to display the data collected with the Bridge Inspection survey you built earlier. As you recall, that app has a field recording the overall status of the bridge (Open or Closed) as well as fields noting guardrail damage, structural damage, pavement condition, and presence of debris. You even created a View of the data that was not editable so that it could be shared with the public … in a dashboard.

1 **Start AGOL and login. In the Content tab find the Survey – County Bridge Inspection folder.**

In this folder are several feature layers, but remember that they all point to the same data because two of them are "views" of the data set for public access. You will use the County Bridge Inspection_Stakeholder layer for the dashboard. There's also some set up involved before the dashboard will really show anything. First there needs to be some data in the layer. If you didn't get a chance to go out and try this Survey 123 App when you first made it, now would be a good time. Alternatively you could open the layer either in an editable AGOL map or in ArcGIS Pro and add dummy surveys manually. Try to get 10 or more surveys done.

The other necessary setup is to make and configure a web map for this layer. It can be simple, with a green dot if the status is open and red dot if the status is Closed. Then configure a pop-up. If you want a shortcut, Raffie made a Project Package for you called GISGuidebooks_Exercise_10a that you can use.

2 **If your County Bridge Inspection feature layer has no data in it, use one of the methods described above to add some data. Create the data in your locale so that you can also try the Survey 123 app (if you haven't already).**

3 **Create a simple web map for the feature layer called County Bridges Web Map using the County Bridge Inspection_Stakeholder feature layer. Set the style and configure the pop-up.**

With the data set up, it's time to decide what you want in the dashboard and how you would like to lay it out. Obviously there will be a map panel, and it gets added to the dashboard automatically. Then you should probably have a count of how many inspections have been made. Then a gauge showing how many bridges are closed as compared to the total of inspections. And maybe a list or two showing which bridges have debris over the road or which ones have guardrail damage. As the elements are added you can try different placement strategies to see how the columns or rows work out.

4 **Open the Items Details for the County Bridges Web Map, then click Create Web App > Dashboards.**

5 **Provide a title of *County Bridge Operations Dashboard* with appropriate tags and summary. Click OK.**

The new dashboard is created and by default a map element with your feature layer is added.

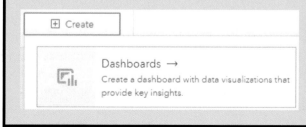

Rafael's Question – We always start our web apps from the Item Details but you said there was another way. Can I try that?

Certainly. From the Content tab, click Create > Dashboards. But you will have to add your own map element if you want a map in the dashboard. If, however, you aren't putting a map in the dashboard then this is how you would start.

After filling out the title entry page and clicking OK, a blank dashboard opens. This is exactly the same as the other method except that your map element isn't automatically added. You can add and configure one with the Add Element button.

Now that you're seeing your dashboard for the first time there are a few housekeeping items to discuss. First, the extent of the map is always locked to the extent of the web map from which you made the dashboard. There is no dashboard control for the extent like there was for Web AppBuilder. If someone edits the source web map and saves it with a different extent, then the extent of the dashboard will change. You can pan the map within the dashboard, but next time you refresh it'll go back to the web map's extent. So be careful about that.

Under the dashboard settings, there is a selection for a Dark theme or a Light theme. Many people prefer the dark theme if the dashboard will be projected in the EOC to cut down glare, but just as many like the light theme. This book will use the light theme only because it will print better. The choice is yours. When you chose your theme preference, you can also set all of the colors used by the elements and other dashboard components. There are a lot and you should probably have a few dashboards under your belt before customizing to this point so that you don't wind up with gray text on a red background (which is not readable).

The Dashboard options has some useful info. It will let you know if any of the data you have included in your dashboard (typically from the Living Atlas) requires an ArcGIS Online login. This can be important if you intent the dashboard to be viewed by the general public. It also has a super short link to the URL for you dashboard making it very easy to share, even if people have to manually type the address.

It's time to start adding elements, with the count of inspections being the first. This will use the Indicator element.

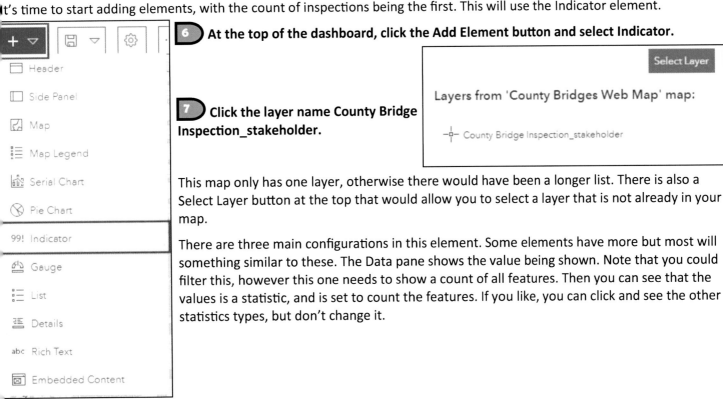

6 **At the top of the dashboard, click the Add Element button and select Indicator.**

7 **Click the layer name County Bridge Inspection_stakeholder.**

This map only has one layer, otherwise there would have been a longer list. There is also a Select Layer button at the top that would allow you to select a layer that is not already in your map.

There are three main configurations in this element. Some elements have more but most will something similar to these. The Data pane shows the value being shown. Note that you could filter this, however this one needs to show a count of all features. Then you can see that the values is a statistic, and is set to count the features. If you like, you can click and see the other statistics types, but don't change it.

8 **The Data configuration doesn't need to change for this element. Click the Indicator tab.**

The Indicator configuration pane lets you set up how the value will be shown within the element. There are three rows of text that can be displayed here, and these can contain regular text as well as values from the feature layer's table. Traditionally the top and bottom text are sized as Medium and the middle text is sized as Large – but you can set these any way you like. The middle text also includes the variable {value} which is the result of the settings on the Data tab, and that variable can also be included in any of the text lines. One thing to now, however, is that if the value is null, none of these rows of text will display. Instead the box will have small gray letters stating "No Data". The example above showed an indicator box with no data.

For each line of text, you can add data field values, set the text color, set the text halo color, and set the text size.

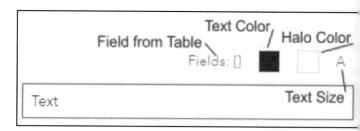

You can also add an icon to the indicator, which can hep identify the purpose of the number at a distance. If this were displayed on the wall in the EOC and seen from 25 feet, it might be good to include an icon so that the data is easier to understand.

9 Set the Bottom Text to *Inspections completed*.

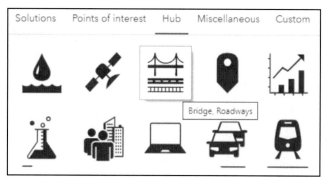

10 Change the Icons setting to Right, then under the HUB category select Bridges and Roads.

When an icon is selected, two color boxes appear on the Icon row. One sets the icon color and the other sets the icon halo. There is also a new box to change the icon.

11 Use the color box to change the icon color to dark blue. Inspect the results.

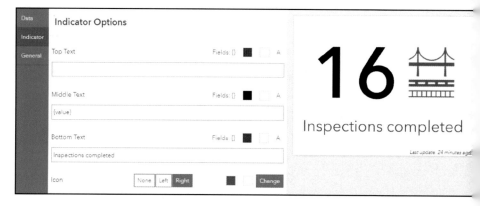

12 Move to the General tab.

The General tab lets you configure things that are not related to the actual data value, but rather to the element itself. The Name setting is for internal use if you were to put this in your own portal and manage it programmatically. For AGOL use you can always accept the default.

The Title text will always show in the element, even if the data value is null. It's a good idea to always have a title so that even when it's empty the box will always identify what it is showing. A description can also be added, which will appear at the bottom of the element. There are controls to turn the title and description on and off. You can also configure the text color of the title and description (even if it's a different color than the value) and set a background color. Also you may notice in the element there is a note saying when the data was last updated. You can turn that line of text on or off. If the data is static, such as population counts, then it would be best to turn this off. If the data is active and always changing, though, you could turn this on.

Then there is a setting for the No Data text. As you saw earlier, if the data value is null the box will display 'No Data' , but you can set this to be something more informative. Remember that the people using and viewing your dashboard may not be map literate, and are trying to get a grasp of the data at a glance. Any assistance you can give with text and color will be very much appreciated. There are many little tweaks and settings involved in each of these elements, and it pays off to click a few just to see what they do. When they all work together they can make the element look sleek and professional as opposed to having glaring color or text issues.

For this element, you will set a title and a background color.

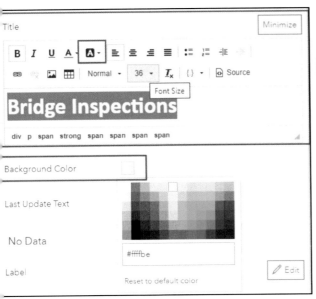

13 Click the Background Color box and select a light yellow. Next click the Edit box next to Title and add the title Bridge Inspections. Make the text bold and increase the size to 36. The icon with the A in a black box is the text formatting tool for the background color – set it to Automatic so that it is the same yellow as the background. When completed, click Done. Then save the dashboard.

As expected, you get one giant element with a number in the middle. That's what is supposed to happen - there's no way to float a small box in the dashboard. It will get smaller as you dock other elements with it.

Next will be to add a gauge showing what percentage of bridges are closed. This will use the statistic of counting the number of bridges that are closed and displaying them in relation to the total number of bridges. When all the bridges are open, this gauge will read 0%. First you will add and configure a gauge, then you will drag it into position in the dashboard.

14 From the Add Element drop down menu, select Gauge. Click the County Bridge Inspection_stakeholder layer.

The default gauge shows the total count of inspections over the fixed value of 100. This needs to be the count of closed bridges over the total count of inspections. You can achieve this by setting a filter on the display value, and changing the maximum value to a statistics showing total count.

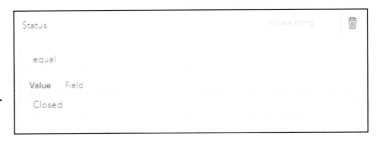

15 In the Data options pane, click Filter. Build the expression 'Status equal Closed'. The Value Type using the count statistic is correct so that can remain unchanged.

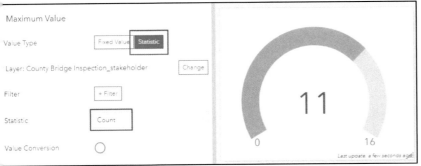

16 The minimum value of 0 is fine. Scroll down and set the Maximum Value to Statistics using Count. No filter is needed since you want the total count.

17 Save the dashboard, then move to the Gauge tab.

The configurations on this pane allow you to set the style, shape, colors, and even change from a count to a percentage. The Progress style shows a colored band filling in as the value changes, while the Meter selection is a graduated circle with a needle pointer. The other options affect the colors used.

18 Review the settings to see what might be available. All of these default settings are fine, so move to the General tab.

Just like the other element, the General tab can control a title, description, colors, and the appearance of the 'last update' text.

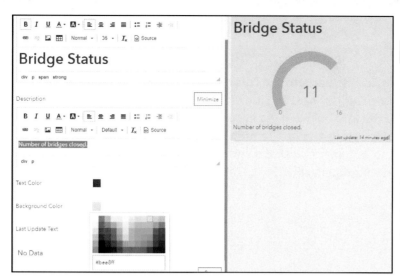

19 Change the title to *Bridge Status* using the same font and size as the last element, then change the Description to *Number of Bridges Closed*. Set the background color to light blue. When completed, click Done and save the dashboard.

A giant box with a huge gauge is added. Now it's time to start stacking the elements. Just like docking windows in Pro, you can dock elements to either side, top or bottom, or even covering another element.

If you drag it one of the edges, it will be spliced onto the existing element and start to form a row or column, each element becoming slightly smaller. If you drag it covering an existing element, the two will then occupy the same space but be revealed by clicking a tab at the bottom.

To drag an element, look for a little blue bar in the upper left when you hover over the element. Clicking this bar will reveal an options menu with the drag tool, the configuration tool, the duplicate tool, and the delete tool.

20 In the upper left of the gauge element expose the options tool. Then click and hold the Drag Item tool and drag the element to the bottom of the Indicator element and on top of the docking icon until it docks and reads Dock As Row. Then let go of the drag tool. You can grab the side of the column to adjust the width and grab the bar between the elements to adjust their sizes.

Don't worry too much about the sizing at this point. As you add more elements all of these things will push and pull each other to fit the situation. Then when you are total done you can set all the sizes one final time.

You may have also noticed that the element's fonts are different (look at the g in Bridge). These are set by default and can't be changed – so learn to live with it. Don't spend an hour researching this like Rafael did.

The last thing to add is a list of bridges with debris on the road so that the debris removal team can see where they need to go. There should also be a list of bridges with guardrail damage for the guardrail repair team. How will each list know what to show? One word … FILTER. You can add these two lists, then work on arranging them in the dashboard.

21 From the Add Element menu, select List. Then select the layer name to open the configuration box.

Right now the list just has symbols in it … don't worry, the text gets added in a minute. You do need to set the filter to just bridges with debris on the road deck.

22 In the Data Options pane, click Filter. Set the filter to 'Debris equals Debris on Bridge Deck'. The rest of the options can stay unchanged.

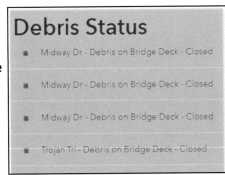

23 Move to the List Options pane.

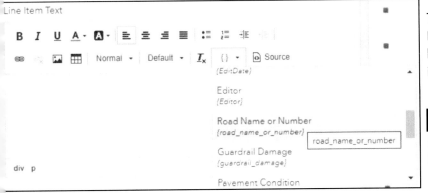

This is where you define what will show in the list. Note that this is formatted as rich text, so you can have images and all kinds of things in here, including values from data fields.

24 In the Line Item Text box click the curvy braces icon to add a field value, then click on Road Name.

25 Next add the field values Debris and Status to the text box and separate them with dashes.

{road_name_or_number} - {debris} - {status}

26 Go to the General tab and add a title *Debris Status* with a similar text style and size as the other elements. Set the background color to a light red.

Debris Status
- Midway Dr - Debris on Bridge Deck - Closed
- Midway Dr - Debris on Bridge Deck - Closed
- Midway Dr - Debris on Bridge Deck - Closed
- Trojan Trl - Debris on Bridge Deck - Closed

27 Move to the Actions tab.

Actions are things associated with the line items in the list that can control what happens in the map. Clicking on a line item can trigger the map to flash the feature, zoom or pan to the feature, open the pop-up box, or set a data filter to include only this feature. You can also configure this to allow selecting multiple lines in the list. Adding an action is a two-step process. Step one is to add the action, and step two is to identify the target map of the action.

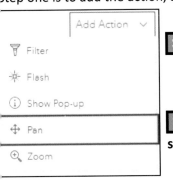

28 Click Add Action and select Pan.

29 In the new Pan box, click Add Target and select the map (there's only one but you can see where this could work with multiple map panes). When completed, click Done.

Another big box to deal with. You can wait until the last element is added before dragging this one around.

The last thing to add is another list showing guardrail damage, and the only difference between it and the one you just made is the title and filter. So you can copy the list, make a few changes, and have it completed in no time.

30 Click the blue options drop down menu in the list element and select Duplicate.

31 Open the Configure pane for the new list. Change these things:

◊ **Filter for 'Guardrail Damage equal Yes'**

◊ **Replace {debris} with {guardrail_damage} in the in the list item text**

◊ **Make the title *Guardrail Status***

32 Click Done.

If you spread things out a bit, you have a four elements with a thick white border between them, and a sliver of a map on the side. It would be ideal to put the two lists side-by-side without a border, then the gauge and total side-by-side without a border, then drop the two lists under the gauge and total.

When you combine elements you have a choice to dock them together, which creates a border, or Group them together which produces no border. Then once grouped, the elements can be moved as one. To group items, begin dragging an element, then hold down the Shift key. Normally the docking preview is a blue box, but when you hold the shift key the preview turns green indicating that you are grouping the elements. The accompanying text also supports this action. Docking (blue) and Grouping (green).

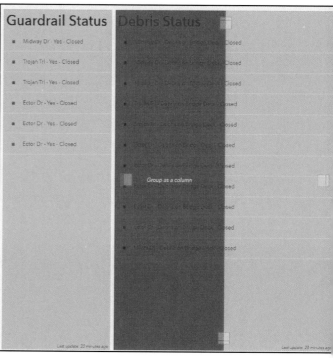

33 Open the options menu and start dragging the Guardrail Status list to the Debris Status list, then hold the shift key and group it to the left side of the element.

34 Group the Bridge Status Gauge to the left of the total count element.

35 Now drag the group and dock it to the top of the lists.

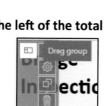

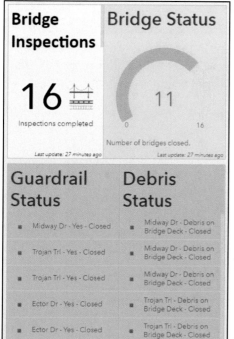

36 Drag the border lines between the elements and groups to make every display nicely and be readable. Note that the columns don't have to line up. Save the dashboard.

The dashboard is looking pretty slick! There may even be a few things to sharpen it up even more. For instance, a legend would look good. There's only two colors of dots, and they represent open and Closed. A title bar would also add something. There are elements for both of those things, but here's the problem. The Header Bar goes across the entire top of the dashboard and in this instance it should probably just go over the map pane. And the Legend element includes the layer name, which for this map isn't very nice looking and there's no way to remove that.

I could drop both those things in and live with it, or I could drop in a Rich Text box and build my own custom title with a built in legend. The Rich Text box can include an image by URL link, so before you try this make and image of the legend item and set up a link to the image.

County Bridge Inspection_stakeholder

■ Closed

■ Open

37 From the element menu, add a Rich Text box. Add a map title, subtitle, image, and whatever else you like. Click Done. Then group the item to the top of the map pane.

The dashboard is finished! You can still adjust the sizes of the boxes but you will find that anything you slide over has to pop out somewhere else. It's hard to get all the text the exact same size (especially when they are different fonts) and this will display differently depending on the device upon which it is viewed.

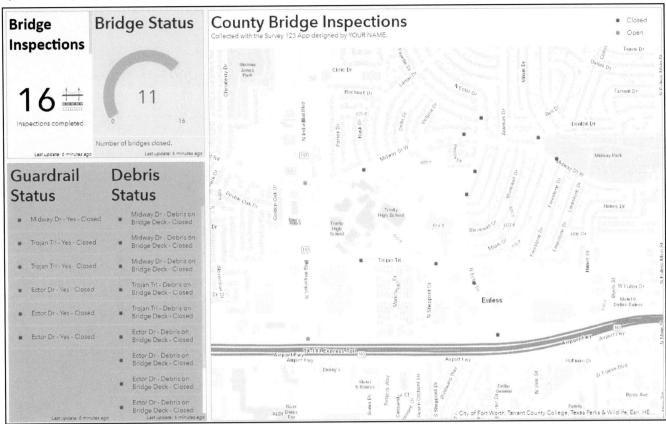

38 Save the dashboard and return to the Content tab. Then open the dashboard in a new window (not in edit mode) and check it out! If any of the columns or other elements seem too big or too small, make a note and go back to tweak the sizes a bit. Zoom in to an area and try clicking an item on the list and making it pan. Add more items to the map, or change the status of some of the bridges to see the changes in the dashboard.

Note that in the upper right of each element group is a little 4-way arrow icon. This will expand/contract the element to fill the entire browser window. Try clicking it on a few of the elements.

39 Close the dashboard and if you are not continuing, exit from AGOL.

This dashboard provides a quick way to review the field work being done on the bridges, but it's the attention to detail that will make the dashboard stand out. The icons, graphic displays, and legends add a cartographer's touch to the overall look and feel.

The Web-based Dashboard Designer Beta

There is also a web-based design interface similar to the ones you used for QuickCapture and Survey 123 available for Dashboards. The Dashboards Beta site is located at arcgis.com/apps/dashboards/, note the word Beta in the logo. There are some differences with the formatting so once you open a dashboard in the beta version you cannot go back. A warning stating this will be displayed and you are encouraged to save a copy of the dashboard.

One of the most important new features is the addition of Arcade expressions in some of the elements. You have the ability to use Arcade expressions to control the text, colors, outlines, background colors, and more so that the look and feel of the elements can react to the values being calculated. For example, an indicator showing the percentage of capacity can have the background turn from green to yellow to red as the percentage grows. Or perhaps make the text turn colors and get larger, or calculate values not included in the database such as elapsed time or the average of several values. Currently only the Indicator and List elements support Arcade expressions but the other elements will also get this functionality soon.

For the List and Indicator elements, a block of Arcade variables have been added that control colors and text, depending on the element. In the image below from a List element's Arcade block, the return{} statement contains all these variables. By adding some calculations above this block, and in this instance an Iif statement is checking the size of the value, you can substitute a conditional value for a color value within the element. In this example, if the value is over 200 the list displays the values in white text over a red background. Otherwise the colors are reversed. We're not going to use the Dashboard Beta in an exercise, but you can try it with the challenges at the end of the book (if you know some Arcade).

```
1   var HighValCol =
2   IIf($datapoint.Day1 > 200, 'red', 'white')
3
4   var HighValTextCol =
5   IIf($datapoint.Day1 > 200, 'white', 'red')
6
7 * return {
8     textColor: HighValTextCol,
9     backgroundColor: HighValCol,
10    separatorColor:'',
11    selectionColor: '',
12    selectionTextColor: '',
13 *  // attributes: {
14     // attribute1: '',
15     // attribute2: ''
16    // }
17  }
```

More Dashboard Elements

There are more elements available in the Dashboard that you can add and configure (and we won't get to them all) and some of them are used to give the user better control over what is being seen. As you saw with the last dashboard, the action is really taking place in the field as data is being collected using Survey 123. Imagine that bridge inspection dashboard being a giant, static display on the wall of the EOC and everyone looking at it from a distance to check the current operational status. Some dashboards, however, have the actions taking place at the desktop where the user makes selections to change what is being shown in the dashboard. Each user can have the dashboard tell them customized answers to their queries as they explore the data.

This type of control is done with action items that are associated with an element. You saw one in the list element where clicking on a list item will pan the map. These can also appear in the Header and Sidebar elements. As the names imply, the Header is an element spanning the top of the dashboard, and the Sidebar is an element that spans the left side of the dashboard. They are fixed to these positions, although you can configure the Sidebar to slide open and closed. Both have titles and other text items similar to what you've seen with the configurations in other elements. The title is a bit more robust, also having the ability to add a logo (with a hyperlink), a background image (also with a hyperlink), and free-standing text (with … you guessed it … a hyperlink). These are all configurable items you've seen before.

But the components of these elements you haven't seen before are the Selector items. These appear as an input dialog that the user sets to filter the data based on their choice. These are the Category Selector (filters on a text string), the Number Selector (filters on a number), and the Date Selector (filters on a single or inclusive range of dates). Each of this can also trigger one or more actions, including filtering the data, zooming, or panning. You can even string these together and have one selector filter the choices for the second selector. For instance if you had a layer of all states and counties in the US and wanted to look up counties, you could have a selector that lets the user pick the state then apply that filter to a second selector to pick the county.

Each selector element has two configuration tabs, the Selector tab where you set up how the selector will get the value, and the Actions tab where you define what will happen to the map when the selection is made. The Selector tab can get a little complex, just remember that the goal is to establish a selected value of text, number, or date, then pass that value on to the Action tab. The value can be a list you build or values from fields in a layer, and there are several ways to format them. For instance, you may have a list of state names shown as radio buttons and the user clicks one, or you could set a dropdown box containing the list, or in the case of dates have a calendar open. There are lots of options, so examine the configurations closely to make sure you understand what the outcome will be. A preview window will help as you build these showing your choices and values.

Since configuring selectors can get a little complex, and building a complete app that also includes a selector would be time consuming as you are learning, the next few exercises will let you build some sample apps that focus on the use of a selector. Then in the challenges at the end of the book you will be able to build a selector into a fully developed app.

In this exercise you will build an app to find (and zoom to) nursing facilities using their name from a pick list. The Nursing Facilities web map that you built before using the HIFLD data has this information, and if you recall is already filtered to show only the facilities in Texas. Even then, a pick list of all the nursing homes in Texas would be huge so you will add controls that let the user narrow the search down by county before presenting the list of names. And to add a twist this app will only be used by the Fort Worth / Dallas hospital district, so they only want to see the facilities in one of these four counties: Dallas, Tarrant, Collin, and Denton. This will be presented in a side panel that is always visible.

You will start with creating a new dashboard using the Nursing Homes Web Map.

1 Start ArcGIS Online and log in, if necessary. **Open the GIS Guidebooks folder and open the Item Details for the Nursing Homes Web Map.**

2 Click **Create Web App and select Dashboards. Provide the title** *Select Nursing Facilities by County and Name* **with an appropriate summary and tags.**

3 Using the **Add Element dropdown menu, add a Side Panel.**

The first view of the configuration is very simple, letting you set the basic title, description, and colors of the panel. Note also the Slide Over Panel tool. With this on the panel will retract from view when not in use, although you will keep the panel visible in this app.

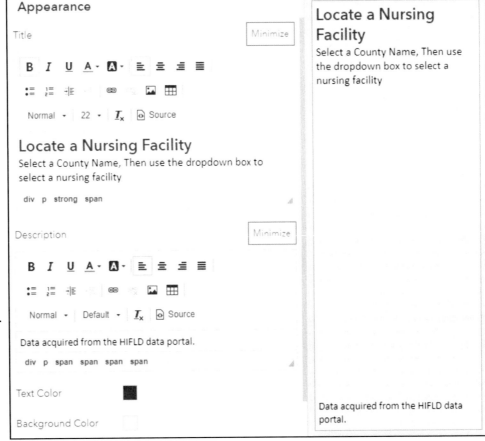

4 Make the Title *Locate a Nursing Facility* **in bold, 22 point text. Then below that add a line of 16 point, non-bold text which reads** *Select a County Name, then use the dropdown box to select a nursing facility.* **Finish by adding a description of** *Data acquired from the HIFLD data portal.* **Change the background color if you like but remember to change the background color of the text to Automatic.**

5 When everything is looking good, **click Done.**

Oh, but you are far from done with the configuration! The blue configuration menu in the upper left will show the selectors that can be added. Each of these will be demonstrated in the next few exercises so that you will get a good understanding of how each is configured, and how it will function in the final dashboard configuration.

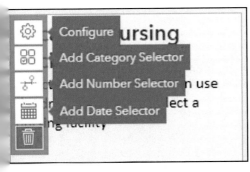

You can add multiple selectors to a side panel, and you will see how to have them work in tandem to make selections. They could also be used to control different layers, but be careful that the actions you configure aren't conflicting.

In this exercise you will add a Category Selector.

6 Click the menu and add a Category Selector. The Selector Options configuration screen will open. Take a moment to glance over the settings—most will be obvious as to what they control.

The configuration of a selector is done in three steps. First in the Data area you will define what data the user will interact with to make the selection. For example, are you going to provide a set list that you type in, or present a list of values from a field for the selection? You can even have the selector do a summary on a field and select a group of values. In this case, you will provide a list of four county names on radio buttons that the user can click – Denton, Dallas, Collin, and Tarrant.

Selector Options

Data

Categories From   [Defined Values] [Features] [Grouped Values]

Value Type   [String] [Integer]

Value   Display Name
No Values Defined

[+ Add]

Selector

Label   [   ]

Selection   [Single] [Multiple]

Operator   equal

Preferred Display Type   Dropdown

Display Type Threshold   10

None Option   ○

Default selection

General

Name   Category Selector (1)

7 Leave the Categories From setting to Defined Values and the Value Type to String. Click the +Add button and type in *Denton* as the Value and *Denton County* as the Display Name. Then click +Add and one-by-one add the other three county names. Make sure you put them in the order you want because you can' t move them later.

Value	Display Name	
Denton	Denton County	🗑
Dallas	Dallas County	🗑
Collin	Collin County	🗑
Tarrant	Tarrant County	🗑

[+ Add]

That takes care of setting the values the user will be able to select. Next is to configure how they will be presented in the menu.

8 In the Selector area, set the Label to 1. Pick a County and leave the selection to Single. Leave the Operator set to Equal, then change the Preferred Display Type to Radio Buttons. Finally, set the Default Selection to Dallas County. Check out the preview pane and try clicking the buttons.

You can see that you could have allowed the user to select more than one county from the list or added a None option. The None option would open the dashboard with no counties selected, and allow the user to return to that status at any time. Neither of those is right for this app. The Operator control can also have different options with other value types. For instance with a numeric selector you can make the selection all values greater than or less than the user's selection.

Selector

Label   1. Pick a County

Selection   [Single] [Multiple]

Operator   equal

Preferred Display Type   Radio buttons

Display Type Threshold   10

None Option   ○

Default selection   Dallas County

The last area to configure is the General area. Normally you wouldn't need to worry about what an element is named, however in this case you will need to reference it in another selector.

9 Change the Name to *County Selector*.

General

Name   County Selector

[Done] [Cancel]

This completes the setup for the value selection. The Action tab will determine what happens when the user selects a value. This selector will act upon another selector so that can't be set yet.

10 Click Done and save the dashboard.

Narrowing the list of nursing homes by county will still display a lot of features, so you should narrow the search by city name, too. A second Category selector can do this with a similar set-up using the values from the field City. Except this time you will use the Grouped Values category type so that will group together all the features with the value you select.

11 Use the Side Panel menu to add another Category Selector. Set the Categories From value to grouped Values and select the Nursing Homes layer.

12 Set the Category Field to City. Note the Sort By field but don't change it.

13 In the Selector area set the label to *2. Pick a City*. The rest of the values are OK.

14 In the general area set the Name to *City Selector*. Click Done.

Once again you can't set an action until the last selector is configured. If you were to look at the Pick a City selector's dropdown list you would see that it contains all the cities in Texas (the first choice of Abilene is not in the four counties you used). By setting the target of the County Selector to City Selector, one will restrict the values of the other.

15 Open the configuration pane for the County Selector item. Go to the Actions tab.

16 Click Add Target and choose City Selector from the list. Set the Filter Field to County. Click Done.

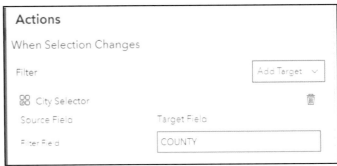

The last thing for this configuration is to add a selector that allows the user to pick a nursing home by name. This can be done with a simple field selection.

17 Add another Category Selector to the Side Panel. Set it to use Features and the Nursing Home layer.

18 At the far right of the Line item Text box click the Fields: {} button. Select Name.

19 Set the Sort By to NAME.

20 In the Selector area set the Label to *3. Pick a Nursing Home*. Change the slider to allow a Null Option. The rest of the values in this area are OK.

21 In the General area change the Name to Name Selector.

Since this is the last selector in the chain you can go ahead and set the actions, and in this case there can be multiple actions. You will need to set a filter action, then you can have it pan to the location and open the feature's pop-up as other actions.

22 Click the Actions tab. Click Add Action and select Filter.

23 Click Add Target and select Nursing Homes.

24 Click Add Action again and select Pan. Then click Add Target and select Map(1).

25 Next, click Add Action and select Show Pop-up. The target will be automatically set.

If you test out the app you'll see that it is showing every nursing home. Now is the time to string the three selectors together.

26 Open the configuration for the City Selector and go to the Actions tab.

27 Click Add Target and choose Name Selector. Click Done.

28 Finally, open the configuration for the County Selector and go to the Actions tab.

29 Click Add Target, choose City Selector, and set the Filter Field to Name. Click Done and save the dashboard.

Now all three selectors are fully configured. After you pick a county, the city selector's dropdown box will only show cities in the county. Then you select a city, the nursing home selector will only display nursing homes in that city.

30 Zoom the map in so that the pan will be more apparent. In the Side Panel, pick Denton County, Pilot Point, and Pilot Point care Center.

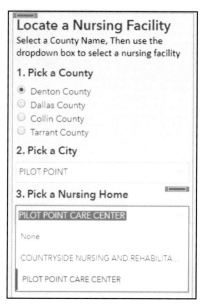

Try some others and note that the final pick list is usually filtered down pretty small, making the selections easy. It took a bit of faith that each selector would play nice with the other selectors but in the end the results are worth it. When building these, have a good idea of the finished product so that you can keep track of what controls what. In this case numbering the selectors in the pane helped.

If you like, try out the dashboard in a regular browser window rather than the editing window. You may see some tweaks you would like to make, and feel free to do so.

31 Go back to the Dashboard edit window if necessary. Click the Add Element button and add a Header. Note the items that can be configured in the header (feeling adventurous, configure a few). Accept all the defaults and click Done.

32 Finally, note that the Header configuration menu can also selectors. Just be careful adding them here because of the limited space.

The configuration of selectors, and even the linking of a series of selectors is done exactly the same way in headers. But you will note that there are some minor differences, like not allowing radio buttons which would take up too much room. Instead, headers have a limited number of buttons that can be placed horizontally. The selectors will even control actions across elements, so if the County Selector is moved to the Header element, it can still affect the selectors in the Side Panel.

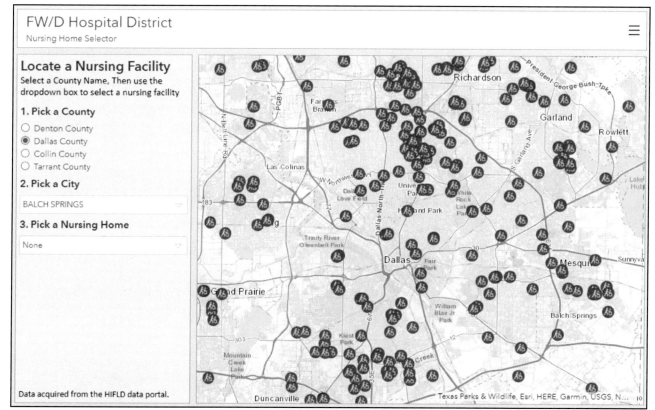

Rafael's Challenge – Move the county selector to the header.

You can't drag and drop it into the header, you have to delete the one in the side panel and recreate it in the header. Make sure to write down all the configuration values from the old selector before you delete it. This was done with the Button Bar option and all the other settings are the same, including the Actions.

More Dashboard Selectors

Another type of selector is the Number Selector. Many of the same configuration settings, such as the title, selector text, and actions, are the same as the Category select. The interface allows you to ask the user for either a single number or a range of numbers that is evaluated against the dataset. The results of the selector, just like in the Category selectors, can be applied to other elements within the dashboard and filter what they can display. For instance you could set up a single entry Number Selector to find an area code, then show a list of cities within that code. Or set up a range entry Number Selector to find houses within a range of values and show the count and total value in some Indicator elements.

Exercise 9c – Dashboard Number Selector

Earlier you made a web map called Daily Covid-19 Count by County. The incident commander wants to be able to view the areas of the state with the lowest total counts as well as the areas with the highest total counts. You will set up a dashboard using that web map and include a Number Selector to allow a selection of a range of values, and a List element to show the results.

If you need to refamiliarize yourself with this data, open the web map and examine the attributes. The field Day 1 is the most current daily count, and you will also use the fields for population and TDEM district.

Take a moment to think about how you might lay this out. The Side Panel has to take the entire left side of the dashboard, top to bottom. And you can't dock other elements either inside or below a side panel. The list will be narrow and tall, so having it down the side will be OK but maybe the Number Selector element needs to go in a header rather than a side bar. Think about how you want yours to look and if it differs from the images here go ahead and build it however you like. No one option is always right and it doesn't hurt to try a few things.

1 Open ArcGIS Online and log in, if necessary. In the Contents tab, find the web map Daily Covid-19 Count by County and open the item details page.

2 Click Web Apps and select Dashboard, giving it an appropriate name, tags, and summary. Click OK.

3 Add a List element to the dashboard. Here's a list of the configuration settings (which you should be able to do on your own).

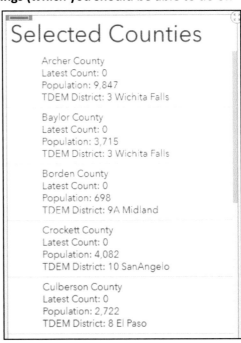

- ◊ **Data: Set the list to use the Daily Covid-19 Count by County layer**
- ◊ **Data: Sort by the field Day 1, then by the field Name**
- ◊ **List: Set the line item text to show the fields {NAME}, {Day1}, {Population}, and {District}, adding descriptive text as you see fit.**
- ◊ **General: Change the name of the element to *County List***
- ◊ **General: Set a 'heading 1' title to read *Selected Counties* and tweak the colors if you like**
- ◊ **Actions: No actions are necessary**

Right now all the values are shown, but that will change when you get the selector added and configured.

121

Add a Header element to the dashboard. Provide a title, subtitle, logos, or other items as you like. Then add a Number Selector element to the header.

If you noticed in the data, the highest value in any county at the time this data was captured was around 7,000 so a range of 0 to 10,000 would be an appropriate selection range. There's also a choice of how you would like the user to manipulate the numbers. Then can use a click arrow, called a Spinner, to change the numbers or be presented with an empty box into which they can type the number. The spinner also allows direct typed entries and also allows you to control the values that are entered. There's even an "increment by" setting so that each click of the spinner advances the numbers by any amount you choose.

The data entry can be either Defined values (numbers you set) or a Statistics (which comes from a field in the dataset). For this project you will have the users click a spinner with a range from 0 to 10,000 and increment by 10. Finally, you will set an Action item to filter the list you made.

The configuration screen will look familiar, so you should be able to follow the instructions below to configure the Selector Options.

3 **In the Selector options pane, set these values:**

◊   **Selector: Set the Input Type to Range**

◊   **Selector: Set the Display Type to Spinner**

◊   **Selector: Set the Limits From to Defined Values**

◊   **Selector: Set the Lower Limit to 0 and the Upper Limit to 100**

◊   **Selector: Set the Lower Default to 0 and the Upper Default to 100**

◊   **Selector: Set the Label to** *Provide a Range of Counts to Evaluate*

◊   **Selector: Set the Increment value to 10**

◊   **Selector: Set the Name to** *Count Range*

◊   **Actions: Add Target > Daily_Covid_by_County_TX**

◊   **Actions: Set the Filter Field to Day1**

◊   **Actions: Add Target > County List**

◊   **Actions: Set the Filter Field to Day1**

 **Click Done and save the dashboard.**

Did you get it all to work? Revisit the configurations if necessary.

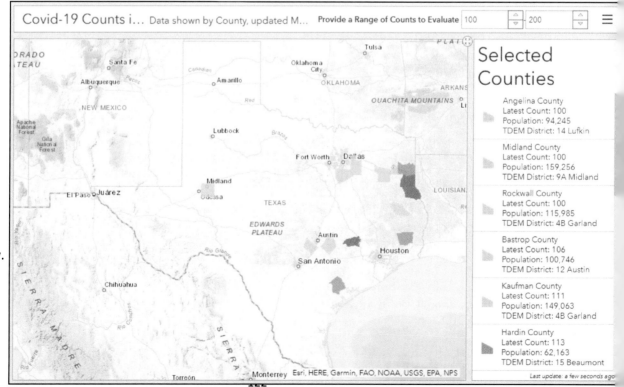

More Dashboard Selectors

You saw in that exercise how another element can be filtered by a selector element, and although that used a list element all the other elements allow this type of filtering. The setup for each is done in the Actions tab in exactly the same manor.

The last type of selector to look at controls dates and times. The Date Selector has many similar features as the other two selector types allowing the user to select from a fixed list, a single value, or a range of values – but in this case dates. There is also a built-in value that can be used to reference the current date called Today. This is helpful when you are needing the selection range to be up to the minute, but don't want to have to update the app every day. For example you could find all the occurrences between a date you set and Today. Then tomorrow get the updated results using a new Today value. Just remember, when you are designing your apps and you want to use dates, make sure there is a date field in the data. Currently there is not a way to use a different type of field as a date value, but they are working on integrating Arcade into these other dashboard elements and that will include the ability to recast a field as a date.

Exercise 9d – Dashboard date selectors

In this practice exercise you will build a dashboard that will look at tornadoes through the years. It's a quick visual analysis not specifically related to disaster response, but it's a good sample dataset with date fields. The Living Atlas has a dataset called Tornado Tracks, and it will be very easy for you at this point to find that data and make a web map from it.

Then you will add that web map to a dashboard and control the display to include a time range. After that you can look at more dashboard elements that you might want to include. Ones you haven't looked at yet include the Details element and the Rich Text element.

1 **Open ArcGIS Online and log in to your account (if necessary).**

2 **Open a web browser and find the Living Atlas page, then search for tornado tracks. Click the options button for the resulting features layer and select Map Viewer.**

3 **Set a filer to only show data in a particular state and you can pick your state of interest – Hint: the Mid-West and Southern states tend to have more tornadoes so any of those would be a better choice than the east or west coasts. Raffie chose Missouri (MO).**

4 **Zoom the map to show your state, then save the map as *Tornado tracks – STATE*.**

Take a minute to look at the attribute table in the map viewer and see if there are any you might like to use in the dashboard other than time. Perhaps for the selected range you could show the count of injuries and fatalities. You could show a details element with the Fujita scale, damage category, wind speed, and tornado intensity. All of the values to be used are in separate fields.

Next take a look at the date formatting. Whoever designed this data split the date and time into 10 separate fields to accommodate a dozen different ways to use dates in analysis. Perhaps they didn't realize that you can extract any of these values from a single date field with Arcade. Note also that there are two fields called Date – the first is formatted as YYYY-MM-DD and the second has the full date/time value. Only this second field is an actual date field with the others being strings and integers. Consequently, only the date field can be used in a Date Selector. You could configure a Date Selector to accept a range of dates, then use that result to filter the other dashboard elements.

5 **Return to the Content tab.**

Rafael's Question – you keep adding feature layers from the Living Atlas, but I also see pre-made web maps and other layers in there. Could I just add those to a dashboard?

Yes you can, but be careful that there isn't already a filter set or symbology that will interfere with your goals. You may also find that the web maps in the Living Atlas are for a larger area than you want to highlight and there is not a way for you to show a smaller area than the pre-set web map shows. You could save a copy of the web map to your own account, in which case you can control filters and visible extents.

To do this, simply click the Save As button and provide a new name and folder. Note that the data is not saved to your account, just the web map configurations. That way when the data is updated, your map of the data is also updated. But to make a dashboard directly from the Living Atlas just click the layer name in the search results and the Item Details page opens. Then click Create Web App > Dashboard just like you would with any other web map.

6 **Open the Item Details for the tornado web map and create a new dashboard. Name the new dashboard *STATE Tornado Analysis Dashboard*.**

The first thing you will want to do is add a header, then add and configure a Category Selector element for the Year field and a Date Selector element for the date field.

7 **Using the add element dropdown box, add a header to the dashboard. Let the title stay the default but set a subtitle that reads *Display Tornadoes within a Date Range*. Make the size Large so that the title and subtitle will appear on two lines. This will also make room for the selector. Click Done.**

Rafael's Question – How can I put a background image in the header?

You saw that there was a place in the header configuration to include a link to an image for both a logo and a background image. You can add an image file to your AGOL contents, share it as public, then include that URL in your header. To try this, you can use the file TornadoImageHeader.jpg provided with the book's materials as the background image. Or use one of your own, making sure that it is suitable for a super wide display. Also be sure to adjust the text image so that it will be visible against the background.

8 **Add a Date Selector to the header.**

You will note that the date selector has a Defined Options just like the other selectors. This might be used if you wanted a pre-set date range (like showing the tornadoes grouped by decade ... Tornadoes in the 1960's, 1970's, 1980's) or a single preset date. But it also has the option to use one of many preset date constants that can find a date as compared to today's date. These constants are:

Today	Last Week	Last Month	Last Quarter	Last Year
Yesterday	This Week	This Month	This Quarter	This Year
Tomorrow	Next Week	Next Month	Next Quarter	Next Year

Plus, by using these constants the actual date to be used in the selection is automatically calculated. If you wanted to have a button that showed values for the past week you could use the Last Week constant and the dates for the selection change every day, meaning that you don't have to change them.

Then of course the Date Picker type allows the user to have full control over the dates selected.

9 **Click the Date Picker type with an Input Type of Range. You can leave the defaults as none so that the user can enter any dates. Add a label *Select a Date Range* and name the selector *Date Range Selector*.**

There is no minimum value setting, so it would be possible that the users could be picking dates that fall well out of range of the data set's values. You could set the lowest available date as the minimum default but that wouldn't stop them from selecting earlier dates. So if you know the lowest value, It's a good idea to document this either in the app's instructions or in the header bar.

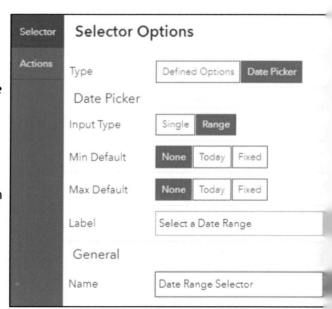

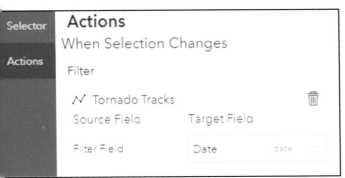

10 Move to the Actions tab and set the action to filter the Tornado Tracks layer using the Date field. Click Done, then save the dashboard.

Using the date selectors can by a little tedious because there are so many aspects to a date and time value. You may want to enter only dates and not time, or you may want to enter both. Or you dates of interest may be 30 years prior to today and scrolling back through the selector might take a long time.

There's not a real fix for this, just be prepared to spend more time working with dates than with normal field values.

By default the selector only shows an entry for date and the time entry is minimized. Clicking the clock icon will open the time entry box, which is controlled by a dropdown box populated with hourly values representing the day. You cannot type a specific time into this box, you must pick from the list meaning that the granularity of your selection is to the hour not to the minute.

The date selector does allow you to type dates directly without having to point to them in the calendar pop-up. You could type in 3/22/1995 for your date and the selector will recognize that.

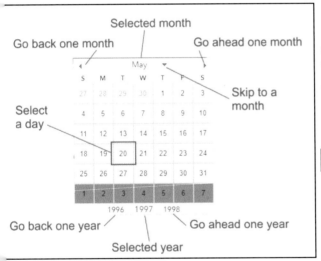

Operating the date using the calendar pop-up has a few tricks to it. The controls within the calendar can help you navigate quickly to a certain year, month or day.

11 Try navigating the calendar pop-up and set some date ranges - note the results. The data values start in January 1950 and go through December 2017.

12 Click on one of the tornado tracks to view the pop-up. These came pre-formatted from the Living Atlas source.

The data shown in the pop-up is what will be shown in the Details Element. This element will display data for each feature selected in a carousel box, and the user can use the controller arrows to view them one by one.

The display can be filtered by the date selector and sorted by a field value. It is very similar to the List Element except that the formatting of the values comes from the pop-up, and only one features is displayed at a time. This means that it can include calculated values and charts – something List Elements can't do. There are other differences, and you could research and compare these two more before deciding which element you might use in your dashboards. For this one, however, you will add a Details Element but because of the amount of data it will display for each feature you will limit the number of features to display to the worst 15 based on the Fujita rating.

EF-3 TORNADO

May 1, 1983; Missouri

Severe Damage
0 Fatalities
3 Injuries

Recorded winds between 136 mph to 165 mph.
Track: 16.00 miles | Width: 1,000 yards

13 Add a Details Element to the dashboard using the tornado Tracks layer.

14 Set the Maximum Features Displayed to 15 and sort Descending on the EF-Scale field.

15 Go to the General tab. Change the name to Detailed Pop-up and set the title to *15 Worst Tornadoes*.

16 Review the other settings and change the colors if you like. Click Done and save the dashboard.

17 Open the configuration page for the date selector and add an action to filter the new details element you added.

Next you will add two indicators, one showing the total fatalities and one showing the total injuries filtered by the selected date range.

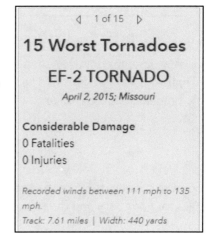

18 Add an indicator and have it display the sum of injuries. Set an appropriate title and associated text.

19 Next, make a duplicate of the indicator element and reconfigure it to show the sum of fatalities. Change the text and colors as appropriate. Group the two indicators together and dock them above the details element.

20 Open the configuration page for the date selector and add filters for the two new indicators. Hint: Use the Actions tab.

That's really looking good, so let's add a few things to make it even better. First, it would be nice to have an image of a tornado displayed in the results column – maybe between the two indicators and the details carousel. There's a public domain image in the book materials that is supplied by the National Severe Storms Laboratory which you can load to your AGOL account and use in the dashboard. There are only a few elements that would display an image: the Header (too small), the Side Panel (can't dock it), and a Rich Text element. This last type of element allows you to build a text display box that can include all types of formatted text, images, tables, and more.

21 Add the *TornadoImage.jpg* file from the book materials to your AGOL account, share it as public, and copy the URL from the Item Details page.

22 Add a Rich text element to the dashboard. Click the Image icon and paste in the URL. Add the text *Image supplied by the NSSF*. Set the image height to 200 (the width will adjust automatically). Click OK.

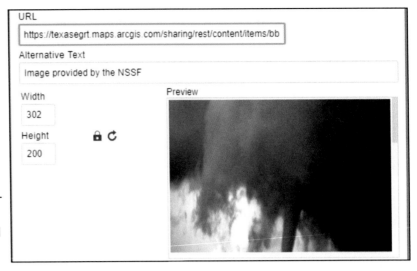

Finally it would be good to have some operating instructions. When you used the Side Panel element before it was to add selectors, but remember that it also allows rich text formatting and can be set to auto-hide off the left side of the dashboard. If this contained operating instructions, it could be very detailed and remain hidden unless summoned by the user.

23 In preparation for the instruction page, add the supplied image CalendarControls.jpg to your AGOL account, share as public, and copy the URL that accesses it.

24 Add a Side Panel element to your dashboard. Give it the title Operating Instructions.

25 Add instructions on how to use the app (and since this is only for practice you can have it say anything you want). Try adding different styles of text, a bullet list, hyperlink, or table, then add the calendar control image. Imagine yourself being the user and try to answer all of the common questions. Then set the Slide Over panel option to Yes. In the Details area, copy/paste the source information from the Living Atlas page where you first found the data. When you have the instructions completed, click Done. Save the dashboard.

You can of course go back and tweak any of the settings in the dashboard. These might include the width and height of the elements, the wording used in the titles and descriptions, and the overall layout. Remember, though, that the dashboard will automatically size itself to the browser size and shape that is being used to view it. The elements and titles may look perfect in your design screen, but be too large or too small when displayed elsewhere. It's a good idea to check your dashboards on the devices that uses will likely have and adjust accordingly.

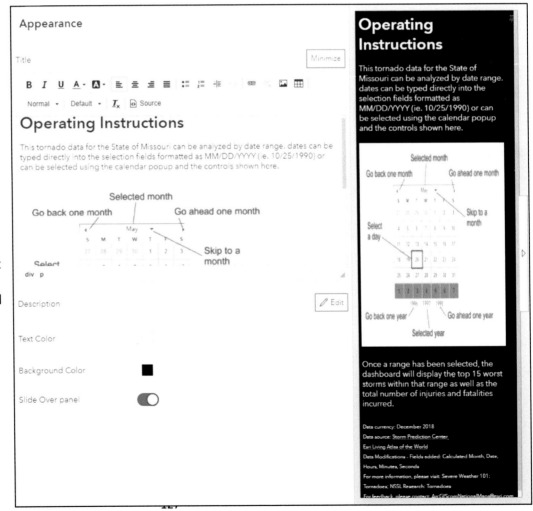

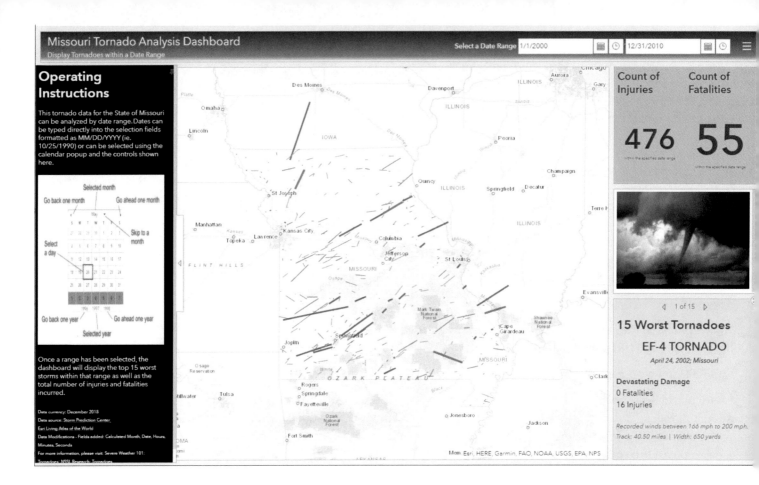

26 **Return to the Content page (saving your dashboard if necessary) and exit AGOL if you are not continuing.**

That made quite a complex looking dashboard (despite Rafael's odd color choices), and in reality you only added and configured a few elements. It's not about the complexity of the dashboard, it's about providing the correct information in a clear fashion. An overly complex dashboard, especially one intended to be a wall-sized display in the EOC, can actually make it harder to find the information users want. If a dashboard gets too complex, consider making two simpler dashboards – but there will always be the situation where there is a lot of info that has to be kept together.

In this example, a side panel was used to hold the operating instructions. If you do this, try to make them as complete as possible and include as much information as possible. Any user questions you can anticipate and answer in this panel will be one less phone call or e-mail you might get about the dashboard's operation.

Chapter 10—Displaying Multiple Web Apps

Before heading into the scenarios, you should take a look at how you might make a briefing atlas for all of the work that you do. When a disaster is in full swing it is hard to disseminate a dozen URL's for web apps to all of the parties involved so EGRT typically makes a CONOPS Atlas.

CONOPS Atlas

Before heading into the final chapter and working through the challenge scenarios, you should take a look at how you might make a briefing atlas for all of the work that you do. When a disaster is in full swing you may have several aspects of the situation that you are handling and obviously all of the data can't go into a single web app. You map have a Common Operation Picture (COP) app that's showing various layers dealing with the current actions, but you may also have web apps for other data collection tasks or planning tasks that would only make the COP app confusing. Instead you may make several apps for each area of the disaster. For instance there may be one situation map showing all actions of the Operations Section, then have another app for the field data collection and summary, and another for local traffic and closed streets for the Logistics Section, or one showing historical actions concerning the disaster for the Planning Section. And it is hard to disseminate a dozen URL's for map apps to all of the parties involved so EGRT typically makes a CONOPS Atlas. This consists of a tabbed Story Map Series into which you can place tabs and pages for all the apps you create. The other advantage here is that if the URL for a map changes, you simply change the page link in the Atlas and everyone automatically gets the new maps in their Atlas under the same URL. As a quick practice, you will create a CONOPS Atlas and place the web apps you've been making throughout this book into it. Obviously these maps don't really have a strong relationship, but it's just practice. Here's the proposed layout:

Page 1 – FtWorth_PW_Management Map App

Page 2 – Daytime Population Summary Web App

Page 3 – TAB 1 - Nursing Homes Summary App

        TAB 2 – Locate a Nursing Facility Dashboard

Page 4 – TAB 1 - Daily Covid-19 Count by County Web App

        Tab 2 – Daily Covid-19 Count by County Dashboard

Page 5 – Missouri Tornado Analysis Dashboard

You need to have at your fingertips the URL's for each map app. These are found on each app's Item Details page and you can copy/paste them into a spreadsheet. It's a good idea to document these in a spreadsheet because you may be the one who initially creates this atlas but it may fall to others later on to add pages or perform maintenance on the atlas. Note that these should be the full URL, not the shortened "Social Media" links.

CONOPS Atlas GIS Guidebooks Exercises			
Page 1		FtWorth_PW_Management Map App	https://texasegrt.maps.arcgis.com/apps/Editor/index.ht
Page 2		Daytime Population Summary Web App	https://texasegrt.maps.arcgis.com/apps/SummaryViewe
Page 3		Medical Facilities	
	Tab 1	Nursing Homes Summary App	https://texasegrt.maps.arcgis.com/apps/webappviewer
	Tab 2	Locate a Nursing Facility Dashboard	https://texasegrt.maps.arcgis.com/apps/opsdashboard/
Page 4		Covid-19 Counts	
	Tab 1	Daily Covid-19 Count by County Web App	https://texasegrt.maps.arcgis.com/apps/webappviewer
	Tab 2	Daily Covid-19 Count by County Dashboard	https://texasegrt.maps.arcgis.com/apps/opsdashboard/
Page 5		Missouri Tornado Analysis Dashboard	https://texasegrt.maps.arcgis.com/apps/opsdashboard/

Exercise 10a—Building a Story Map CONOPS

The first part of this will be to create a tabbed Story Map Series and make the first page (so have the first URL ready). If you recall, the Story Map Series is one of the Configurable Apps templates.

1) Start AGOL and … well you know that part by now.

2) On the Content tab click Create and select Configurable Apps.

3) Find the Story Map Series template and click it, then select CREATE WEB APP.

4) Enter the title of *CONOPS Atlas for Guidebook Exercises* with a appropriate tags and summary. Then click Done. The map Series Builder wizard will walk you through the steps.

The choices of layout are Tabbed, Side Accordion, and Bulleted. If you like, click the Live Example button for each of these to get a feel for how they work. For the CONOPS Atlas you will make the main page a Side Accordion with each page being listed in a vertical column. Then for page that has more than one app to display, such as pages 3 and 4, you will build a separate Tabbed app to hold those apps. Then use the URL of that app for the page in the atlas.

5) Select Side Accordion and click Start.

6) Check your Tabbed Map Series title and click the arrow to continue.

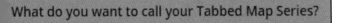

What do you want to call your Tabbed Map Series?

CONOPS Atlas for Guidebook Exercises - Rafael

At this point you are prompted for the information about the first page, including the title and the source. The title should be a few words about what the page contains – later you get to write a full description. The source can be a web map, an image, a video, or a web page (Web App). Displaying a web map would be fine to just display some data or tell a story, except that it is a view-only map with limited tools or widgets. In almost every circumstance you should go ahead and make a web app, even if it has no additional tools. Then later on if you need to add more functionality to the app you have that option. All of the entries for this atlas will be web apps, not web maps.

Also, after you paste in a web app's URL you will add &Embed to the end of it. This will cause the atlas to strip off any extraneous borders from the original web app and make it display more cleanly in the page.

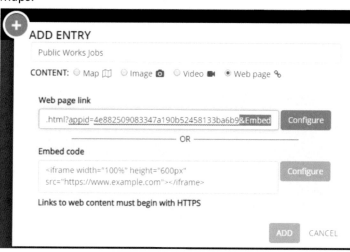

7 Enter the title of *Public Works Jobs*. Change the Content to Web Page and paste in the URL for the first page's web app. Add *&Embed* to the end of the URL and click Configure.

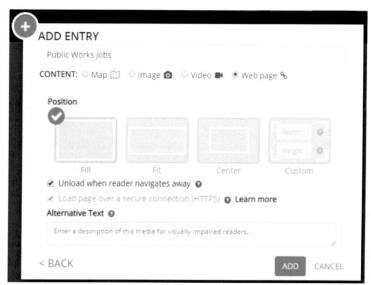

You will want the app to totally fill the atlas page and have it unload each time the reader navigates away from the page. This ensures that every time the viewer opens a page the newest data is added. For regular story maps the data in the pages may not change very often (if at all) but in a disaster the data is constantly changing.

8 Review and accept the default values by clicking Add.

The first map is added in. Notice that the app is configured to have the editing window open automatically when the app opens. This may or may not be what you want in the atlas – you can decide and change it if you like.

With the main framework of the atlas built you can look at some of the app settings to add a more custom look. This is done with the Settings button at the top of the app. Note that these buttons only appear when you are editing the app and would not be visible to the casual user.

9 Click the Settings button at the top of the app display.

This first configuration tab called Layout would let you change the display type in case you change your mind from when you created the app. You can leave that alone.

10 Click the Layout options tab. Set the panel to Left and the size to Small, and verify that the box is checked to display the numbers. Click Apply.

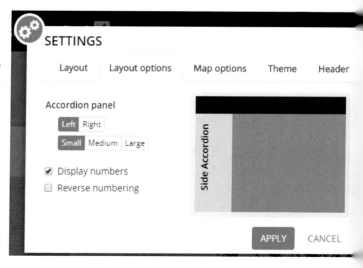

This configuration tab allows you to move the panel to the left or right, change the size, and turn numbering on or off.

Because the maps should be the focus it is common to make the panel small, and with the different maps numbered it is easier to reference them in other reports and documents (including any instructions) you might write.

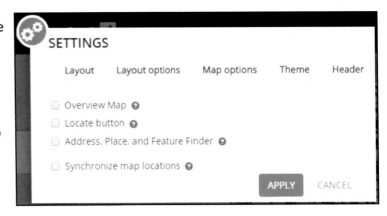

11 **Click the Map Options tab. Uncheck Synchronize Map Locations.**

These allow you to add these controls to every map rather than configure them one by one. They are more useful if you are adding web maps rather then web apps to the atlas, and since you are adding web apps they are not needed. It is also suggested for this type of atlas not to synchronize the map locations from page to page since you may have some maps designed to show local data, some designed to show regional data, and some designed to show national data.

12 **Click the Theme tab and select whichever color you like. Click Apply.**

If you had a common color concept through the web apps, this is where you could set something close to that. There is a gray/black theme that would work well if you are using the dark background themes for dashboards. Otherwise pick a color you like.

13 **Click the Header tab.**

The last tab controls a lot of the little details in the interface. You can keep the Esri logo or add your own (or have no logo at all), plus provide a link with the logo. You can also add a tagline, which is a good place to add a link to your instructions page if you write one. You also have control over the subtitle. These take more room than you might think so to optimize the map display this atlas will not have a subtitle.

14 **Add your own logo (or use the GIS Guidebooks logo from the supplied materials), add any links you might want, and verify that the subtitle will not be shown.**

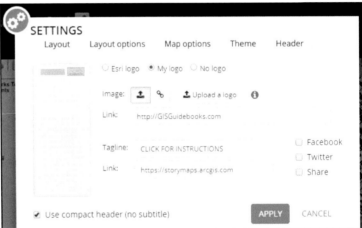

15 **When you are satisfied with all the configuration settings, click Apply. Review the display and make any changes to the configuration that you like. Click Save to save the app.**

Next is to set the sharing. You know the options here, but included in the sharing configuration is a shortened URL and the code to embed this app into a web page.

16 **Click the Share tab and set the sharing to Organization. Copy the URL and paste it into your spreadsheet of web app links. When completed, close the configuration box.**

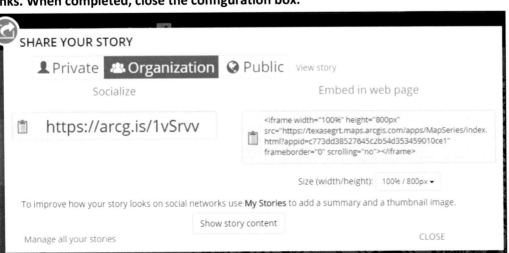

Note that this shortened URL is great for sending around but there are two warning that come with them. The cannot be used with the &Embed code to place this into another page 9captrue the full URL for that), and they are case sensitive.

Having set the overall configurations for the app you can now focus on adding and configuring each map. When you added the first page you saw that there is a place to show a title, which you set when you added the page, and a block of rich text under the title to explain the page. This area will commonly contain a brief description of the data being shown perhaps some simple instructions for using the app. It's also a good idea it add a link to the web app being displayed so that others working the same disaster can include your app in their briefing boards. If you wish to provide more instructions or a link to all the features services being used it is suggested that you do that in a separate document of instructions.

17 **Click the ADD TEXT area for page 1. Write a brief description of the app and add a link to the source web app. Save the app.**

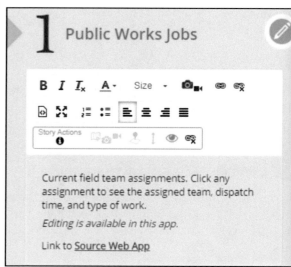

Now you can add page 2. This is done by clicking the ADD button at the bottom of the side panel. The process is exactly the same as adding the first map, but with a different title and web link.

18 **Click ADD to add a second page. Provide the title** *Daytime Population Summary*. **Click Web page and paste in the URL for the page 2 app from your spreadsheet. Click Configure. Verify the settings and finish by clicking Add.**

19 **In the atlas, provide a description of the page 2 app, any instructions, and a link to the source GIS app. Save the app.**

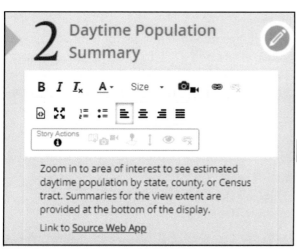

The next two pages will have multiple tabs and require some more intense configurations ... so for now skip those and go on to page 5. When you add this page,

20 **Click Add to add another page. Provide a title, url to the app, check setting, and click Add. Provide a description and instructions.**

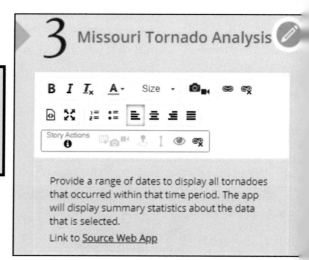

Rafael's Question – Mine went in as Page 3, but the chart says to make that Page 5?

The pages are automatically numbered and you don't have control over that. However once you add the other two pages you can reorder the pages so that this app moves to page 5.

The next page has two web apps to include. To show those you will create another Map Series with two pages, then paste that URL into a page in the atlas. To minimize the amount of screen real estate the apps use, the layout should be the tabbed theme with no side bar.

21 **Open a second tab in your web browser and go to your Contents tab.**

22 **Click Create > Configurable Apps. Find the same Story Map Series template that you used for the atlas and click create Web App.**

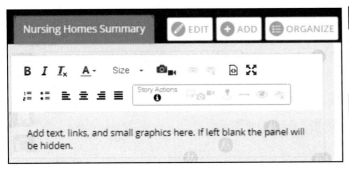

23 Provide the title *CONOPS Atlas Medical Facilities* and add appropriate tags and a summary. Click Done.

24 Follow the same configuration steps you did previously, but use the Tabbed layout and the default title.

25 Create Tab 1 with the title *Nursing Homes Summary*, paste in the URL for Page 3, Tab 1 and click Add.

Each tab will have a drop-down box for a description. Leave these blank! They will clutter up the display, and anything you need to provide the user about the tab can go in the atlas tab for the page. It is best to keep this as simple and streamlined as possible. Add the details that may be needed to the atlas.

You also see similar controls to add another page.

26 Click Add and follow the steps to add the Locate a Nursing Facility dashboard. Save the app.

27 Click the Share button and set the sharing to Organization. Also, copy the URL and paste into your URL spreadsheet.

28 Save and close the app.

29 Return to editing the atlas map series.

30 Add a new page called *Nursing Facilities* using the new URL for the other map series. Populate the description pane as necessary.

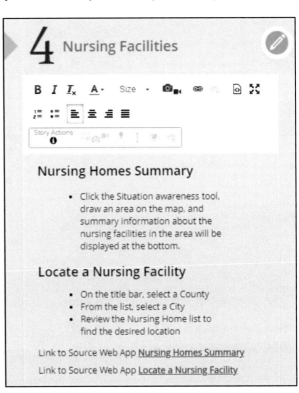

Note that when adding one Story Map as a page into another Story map, you don't need to include the &Embed code at the end of the URL. And remember that the shortened URLs won't accept the &Embed code.

31 Follow the same steps as above to create a new web map series containing the two web apps for page 4.

32 Add a new page to the CONOPS Atlas with the new tabbed map series for the Covid-19 Daily Counts apps. Save the app.

That should finish the compiling of pages into the Atlas. You can go through and test each page, and if any are not displaying correctly check the URL and try removing the &Embed if it was added. This code is not always necessary, and is not always recognized. The pages, however, are not in the correct order.

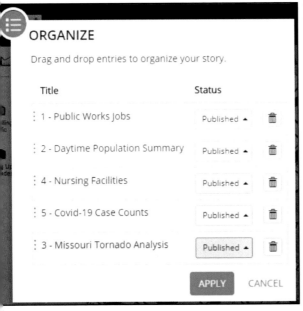

33 Click the Organize button at the bottom of the page list. Drag and drop the pages into the correct order.

Note that there is a delete button (be careful with that) and a Status selector. If you are revamping a page or changing its content this selector will put a page into Hidden mode so that it is not viewable. Once you finish the changes you can publish it again.

The map series can have sharing set different from the apps it contains. However, all of the web apps added to a map series will follow their individual sharing restrictions regardless of the map series settings, So if a password is required for one of the apps, even if the map series is shared as Public the user will see a login box before being taken to the page.

You may also notice that when the atlas is opened by others and a password is required, they will see the Edit button at the top of the app. Clicking this will take them into edit mode where they could alter the contents of the map series. If you don't want that, identify all of the users who you do not wish to give editing privileges and remove their accounts from the same Editing Group as the Atlas.

34 **Make any final modifications you wish, then save end exit the Map Series Builder.**

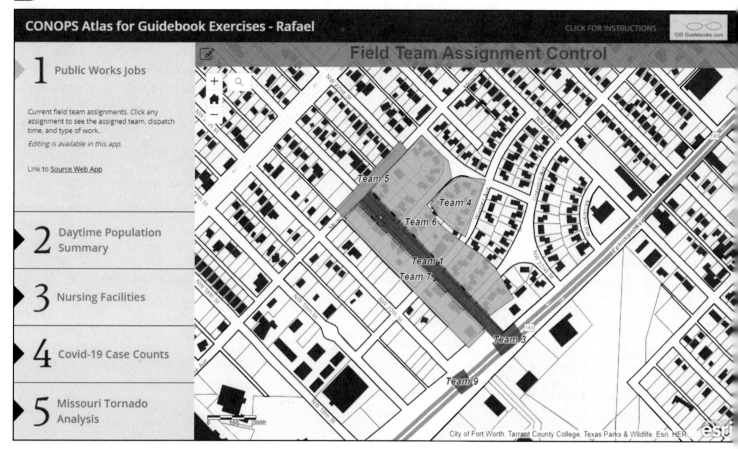

35 **If you are not continuing, log out and close ArcGIS Online.**

It's always a good idea to have someone open and test all the pages in the Atlas before shipping it around to all the responders. If any issues are found either in the page displays, the titles or general wording, or the amount of instruction needed for each app you can get those things fixed. And always remember that the users of these apps are not always seasoned GIS professions like yourself and may require a simple interface and a lot of instructions.

Chapter 11 – Putting It All Together

It's been a journey to get to this point in the book and if you have completed each of the exercises successfully then you must be pretty good with AGOL and the web apps. This last chapter contains ideas on how all of these skills can be put together to create apps that will be helpful in a disaster. The intent is not to have a definitive list of apps that you must create but rather give you practice on designing and making apps. It's important to know and practice all the basics because when a disaster hits you won't have time to research and test tools and techniques. You will need to be able to spin up apps quickly. Sometimes you will find the exact Esri solution for what you want to do and can implement that right out of the box, but many times you will either make these from scratch or make modifications to an existing solution to get a custom app that fills all needs.

Below is a description of each project. Included with the book materials you will find a folder called Chapter 11 which contains a more details write-up of each scenario along with the data necessary to complete them. Then build a CONOPS Atlas showing the results of these scenarios.

Challenge Number 1– Tornado Damage Assessments with Survey 123

You will set up a Survey 123 app for damage assessment using the ATC-45 template. Then create a web map and embed that in an Operations Dashboard so that the results can be displayed in the EOC. Then you can build a web app for editing and summarizing the Survery 123 data and it's attached photos.

Challenge Number 2– Shelter Status Dashboard

Create a dashboard with no map showing the status of the 8 shelters in the supplied dataset. Some are active, and they are all at various levels of capacity. Use the standard Dashboard, but for an extra challenge use the Dashboard Beta and control the background colors based on the active status and the capacity.

Challenge Number 3– Regional Traffic Display

Using the Traffic data from the Living Atlas of the World you will make a map of your tornado region showing the traffic status. You can either use one of the pre-configured templates or Web AppBuilder with custom widgets.

Challenge Number 4– QuickCapture Hazards App

Build a QuickCapture app that can be used to quickly grab the location and a photo of any hazards first responders may encounter in the disaster area. They should be able to mark loose animals, downed power lines, closed streets, and other hazards. Also create a web app for viewing the results of the app in the EOC.

Challenge Number 5– Texas Schools and Districts

Using data from the Texas TEA Data Portal, build a Web AppBuilder app of the schools and school districts. Among the widgets to add is the Situational Awareness app that can summarize schools in a defined area. You will scan the widgets list to find other interesting tools to include.

Challenge Number 6– CONOPS App

Use the tabbed Story Map Series template to create a CONOPS display app for the EOC and other interested responders.

Made in the USA
Monee, IL
25 August 2020